CHEMISTRY AND PHYSIOLOGY OF FERTILIZATION

These Studies are designed to inform the mature student—the undergraduate upperclassman and the beginning graduate student—of the outstanding advances made in various areas of modern biology. The books will not be treatises but rather will briefly summarize significant information in a given field and interpret it in terms of our current knowledge of the rapidly expanding research findings within the life sciences. Also it is hoped that the Studies will be of interest to teachers and research workers.

BIOLOGY STUDIES ←

Alberto Monroy
*University of Palermo
Italy*

CHEMISTRY AND PHYSIOLOGY OF FERTILIZATION

Holt, Rinehart
and Winston
*New York, Chicago,
San Francisco,
Toronto, London*

▶
▶
▶
▶
▶ This volume is dedicated to

ALBERT TYLER

*as a token of friendship
and in memory of a long
and stimulating cooperation*

Ma il seme affinché eserciti la sua azione
nei girini, deve insinuarsi nei loro corpicelli,
sembrando che non possa animarli con la
semplice impressione da esso fatta su la
loro cute.

L. SPALLANZANI. "DISSERTAZIONI DI FISICA
ANIMALE E VEGETABILE" VOL. II, MODENA,
1780.

*However, for the semen to exert its effect
on the eggs, it must enter their little bodies,
as it seems unlikely that it could animate
them by the mere contact with their skin.*

preface ►►►►►

The purpose of this book is to review the present state of our knowledge on the problem of the physiological and chemical basis of fertilization. Less than ten years have elapsed since the publication of Rothschild's *Fertilization;* meanwhile a number of new facts have been discovered which, although they have not really solved the problem, have at least contributed considerably toward indicating quite promising avenues of research. There has lately been a revival of interest in the problem of fertilization among biologists and among biochemists; it is my hope that this book may serve the double purpose of stimulating their interest further and of making their acquaintance with the problem easier.

This book is largely an outcome of the Training Program on the Physiology of Gametes and Fertilization at the Marine Biological Laboratory, Woods Hole, in which I have had the good fortune to participate since 1962. Indeed the unique facilities offered by the Marine Biological Laboratory, the daily contacts with my colleagues and with our students in the course and with the scientific community of Woods Hole, have provided the basis for the preparation of the book. The activating stimulus actually came from my friend Dr. James D. Ebert, who suggested that I embark on this venture. It is to be hoped he will not regret his suggestion.

For the many useful discussions we had and for their comments and suggestions on several parts of the book I wish to express my sincere thanks to Drs. K. Aketa, C. R. Austin, J. Brachet, A. L. Colwin, L. H. Colwin, G. Giudice, P. Gross, H. Grundfest, Y. Ishida, C. Levinthal, L. H. Linskens, R. Maggio, C. Mann, Th. Mann, E. Marré, Ch. B. Metz, G. Millonig, A. Minganti, A. E. Mirsky,

M. Mitchison, L. Nelson, J. J. Pasteels, E. Scarano, and A. Tyler. For permission to quote unpublished results of their work and for supplying unpublished illustrations thanks are due Drs. J. C. Dan, L. Franklin, G. Millonig, A. E. Mirsky, E. Nakano, G. Ortolani, G. Reverberi, and E. Scarano.

For permission to reproduce illustrations from their publications I am indebted to the Academic Press (for reproduction of illustrations from *Archives of Biochemistry and Biophysics, Biochemical and Biophysical Research Communications, Experimental Cell Research, Journal of Ultrastructure Research*), *Biological Bulletin*, Blackwell Scientific Publications (*Journal of Reproduction and Fertility*), Danish Science Press Ltd. (*Comptes Rendus des Travaux du Laboratoire Carlsberg, Série Chimique*), The Editors of *Embryologia*, The Editors of *Endeavour*, The Editors of *Experientia*, Kungla Svenska Vetenskapsakademien (*Arkiv f. Zool.*), Messrs. Macmillan, Ltd. (*Nature*), Messrs. Methuen and Co. Ltd. (Rothschild's *Fertilization*), The Rockefeller Institute Press (*Journal of Biophysical and Biochemical Cytology* and *Journal of Cell Biology*), The Royal Society, London (*Proceedings of the Royal Society, Ser.B*), and The Wistar Institute (*Journal of Experimental Zoology*).

The work of my colleagues and myself in Palermo has been supported by grants from the Italian Ministry of Education, the Italian National Research Council, the Rockefeller Foundation, the National Institutes of Health, the U.S. Public Health Service, and the Department of Health of the Regional Administration of Sicily.

A.M.

Palermo
January, 1965

contents

chapter one

Introduction

In his classic work, *The Cell in Development and Inheritance*, E. B. Wilson wrote: "The essential phenomenon of fertilization is the union of a sperm nucleus, of paternal origin, with an egg nucleus, of maternal origin, to form the primary nucleus of the embryo." This definition indeed outlines the basic feature of fertilization, namely that of bringing together the genetic information contained in the nuclei of the two gametes. This very fact makes of fertilization not only the beginning of morphogenesis but also one of the fundamental instruments of evolution.

In this book only the first aspect of the problem will be discussed: fertilization will be considered only as the incitement to development. It is the aim of the physiological and chemical investigations of fertilization to discover the nature and sequence of reactions which wake the mature egg from its condition of dormancy and eventually lead to development. This first series of events is usually spoken of as the "activation of the egg." Activation need not necessarily be brought about by fertilization. In some eggs under natural conditions, and in practically all eggs under laboratory conditions, it can be obtained through chemical or physical stimuli. Such parthenogenetic activation may lead to complete development, or it may not progress beyond the very early cleavage stages. Even in the latter case, however, it is a very interesting phenomenon, as it proves that the egg is endowed with the necessary machinery to initiate development, when provided with a suitable triggering mechanism. Furthermore, parthenogenesis is a powerful tool for the study of the processes underlying activation, since it imitates fertilization under conditions which rule out the intervention of the usual activating agent, the spermatozoon.

The three main physiological events of fertilization are (a) the sperm-egg interactions before any actual contact is established between the two gametes; (b) the interaction after the establishment of physical contact; (c) the egg reaction to the penetration of the

1

spermatozoon, namely the activation of the egg. Both from the embryological and the genetical point of view, the crucial final event of these reactions is the fusion of the egg nucleus with the sperm nucleus to give rise to the zygote nucleus.

These points we propose to analyze. This account will be based mainly on the eggs of marine invertebrates, and particularly the echinoderm eggs, because it is this material which has provided by far the largest amount of information on the physiology and chemistry of fertilization. The eggs of the echinoderms meet almost all the requirements of an ideal material for the study of fertilization. Firstly, the eggs of several genera of sea urchins are sufficiently small and transparent to be suitable for in vivo microscopic studies. Then these eggs can be collected in large quantities and when fertilized they undergo development quite synchronously. This is an important prerequisite for chemical studies. Finally, although the echinoderm egg is altogether independent of its environment with respect to its nutritional requirements for development, it has been shown to be able to take up a number of organic and inorganic substances added to the medium. This egg can therefore be used in research involving tracer compounds or inhibitors for metabolic studies. On the contrary, other eggs widely used for chemical embryological studies, such as those of the amphibians, are impermeable to substances added from without.

Important data have also been obtained from the study of the eggs of some fishes, notably the Japanese fresh-water teleostean "Medaka," *Oryzias latipes*. These eggs, too, are transparent and lend themselves well to biochemical investigations. A drawback in these as well as in the eggs of some marine invertebrates, the tunicates, which would otherwise be excellent subjects, is the presence of a tough chorion around the egg. Although the chorion can be removed either chemically or mechanically, it makes chemical studies quite difficult.

It is appropriate to consider here a question that may at first appear purely conventional. This is the matter of the time limits of the fertilization process. The establishment of the interaction between egg and sperm obviously marks the zero time. It is more difficult to make a definite statement as to when the process is over. Indeed, once the sperm has entered the egg, a rapid succession of phenomena takes place which eventually leads to a first cleavage. Therefore it is difficult to make a clear-cut or even significant distinction between some of the late events of fertilization and the early ones leading to cleavage. A certain degree of overlapping is almost unavoidable. Strictly speaking, fertilization in the physiological sense should be considered terminated once the spermatozoon has entered the egg and activation has taken place. However, this is, in most cases, a very rapid process. There is a whole series of events, which, although related to activation, are initiated at the moment of the sperm entry, proceeding then at a considerably slower rate. Therefore, from an operational point of view, it seems not unreasonable to consider the fusion of the pronuclei as the closing event of fertilization.

chapter two

The Interaction between Eggs and Spermatozoa

Most animal eggs are surrounded by capsules. These range from a mucopolysaccharide coating to the discrete and often tough membranes with which, sometimes, layers of cells are associated (Fig. 2–1).

The pioneering work of F. R. Lillie (1913, 1914) gave evidence for the first time that egg coats are not just a protection to the egg but may serve an important and indeed a key role in fertilization. In spite of the fact that several of Lillie's conclusions no longer appear to be tenable, his work has had such an impact on the development of research on fertilization that it deserves a pre-eminent position in any discussion on this subject.

LILLIE'S FERTILIZIN

Starting from the observation that the sea water in which unfertilized sea urchin eggs had been standing (so called egg water) *agglutinates* spermatozoa of the same species and transiently *stimulates* their motility, Lillie developed his "fertilizin" theory. This postulates that the unfertilized egg continuously secretes an active substance "fertilizin" which diffuses from the egg and *saturates* the jelly coat; this explains the presence of sperm-agglutinating activity in the egg water, and of the jelly coat dissolved in sea water. Fertilizin furthermore enters into the structure of the egg cortex as an important component. According to Lillie, secretion of fertilizin is stopped at fertilization. Fertilizin was conceived by Lillie as a dipolar molecule, one pole being the ovophile group, the other the spermophile group (Fig. 2–2). Upon fertilization, the

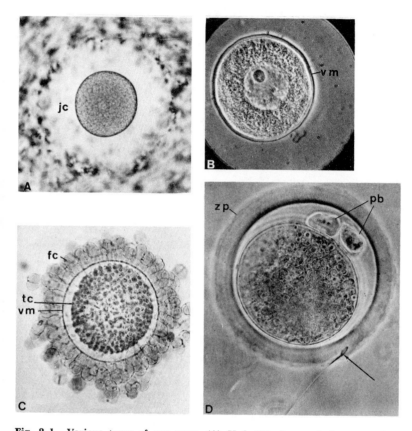

Fig. 2–1. Various types of egg coats. (A) Unfertilized egg of the sea urchin, *Paracentrotus lividus* in sea water to which India ink was added to show the jelly coat (*jc*). (B) Unfertilized egg of the polychaete, *Pomatoceros triqueter;* the vitelline membrane (*vm*) is clearly visible (from Monroy, 1948b). (C) Unfertilized egg of the tunicate, *Ascidiella aspersa:* the egg surface is covered by a layer of test cells (*tc*) and therefore is not visible in the photograph; *vm*, vitelline membrane; *fc*, follicular cells (courtesy of Professor G. Reverberi). (D) Mammalian egg: newly fertilized egg of guinea pig with two polar bodies (*pb*); zona pellucida (*zp*) and a spermatozoon (arrow) excluded as a result of the zona reaction (from Austin and Amoroso, 1959).

receptor sites located at the surface of the spermatozoa react with and bind themselves to the spermophile groups of the fertilizin molecules located at the surface of the egg. This gives rise to a reaction of activation of all the fertilizin molecules at the egg

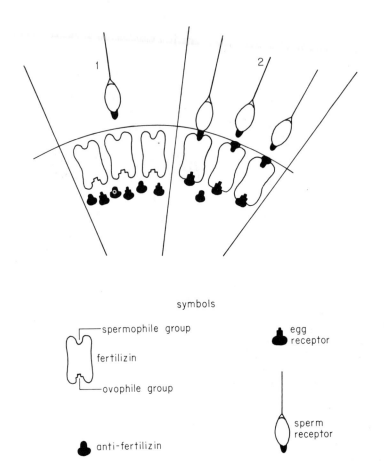

Fig. 2–2. Illustration of F. R. Lillie's theory of fertilization. In the unfertilized egg, fertilizin molecules are present in the cortical layer of the egg. Each one of them bears an ovophile and a spermophile group (Sector 1). Upon fertilization (Sector 2), the sperm receptors of the spermatozoon combine with the spermophile groups of a group of fertilizin molecules (for the sake of simplicity, one sperm receptor per spermatozoon is indicated in the diagram). This reaction activates the fertilizin molecules and the activation propagates all over the egg surface. As a result of such activation, molecules of antifertilizin rapidly block all the spermophile groups of the fertilizin molecules, thus preventing reaction with other spermatozoa: this is Lillie's hypothesis concerning the mechanism of prevention of polyspermy. Another result of the activation of the fertilizin molecules is the reaction of all ovophile groups each with one egg receptor: this is the hypothetical mechanism of the activation of the egg. (Adapted from F. R. Lillie, 1914.)

surface. As a result, their spermophile groups each bind one molecule of antifertilizin (another substance supposed to be present within the egg), thus abolishing the ability of fertilizin to react with further spermatozoa. This, according to Lillie, is the basis for the polyspermy-preventing reaction. On the other hand, the ovophile groups of the activated fertilizin molecules react with the egg-receptors (also present in the egg cytoplasm) and this is the basis of the activation of the egg.

Further development of the investigations into the significance of fertilizin is due to Tyler and his co-workers, who have considerably modified Lillie's original theory (see especially Tyler, 1948*, 1956, 1960). One of the most important early observations was that the egg does not actively secrete fertilizin; this is most likely synthesized in the gonad during oogenesis. Moreover it was shown that fertilizin is probably the only component, or in any case the major component, of the jelly coat: in other words, fertilizin is the jelly coat.

The description that follows will show that the fundamental property of fertilizin, that is, of the jelly coat, is that of causing certain changes in the spermatozoon that enable it to interact with the egg. This property appears to be shared by the mucopolysaccharide egg coats of all forms thus far investigated.

Therefore, for descriptive purposes (also in view of the physiological implication it conveys) it seems advisable to abandon the use of the term "fertilizin" and to speak instead of egg coats.

Before discussing the nature of the interaction between "fertilizin," that is, the jelly coat, and spermatozoa, it seems expedient to consider the chemistry of this substance.

CHEMICAL COMPOSITION OF THE JELLY COAT OF THE ECHINODERM EGG

The jelly coat of the echinoderm eggs is easily dissolved by sea water acidified at pH 5; it can further be purified by a simple procedure worked out by Tyler and Fox (1940) and Tyler (1949). The highly viscous material thus obtained appears to be homogeneous both electrophoretically and in the ultra-centrifuge (Runnström et al., 1942; Tyler, 1949; Tyler et al., 1954; Tyler, 1956).

Whether or not the jelly coat is actually made up of one single molecular species will be discussed later in this chapter.

Electrophoresis shows that the jelly coat is a strongly acidic substance ($u = -18 \cdot 10^{5-}$/cm²/volt/sec); indeed there is practically no mobility change on lowering the pH from 8.6 to 2.0. This acidic character is due to the high content of sulfate groups (Vasseur, 1947 and summary in 1954). At least in the case of the jelly coat substance of *Arbacia*, the molecules appear to be highly asymmetrical, with an axial ratio of about 20/1 and a molecular weight that has been estimated at about 300.000 (Tyler, 1956). Chemical analyses of the jelly coat substance of the sea urchin eggs prove that it is a glycoprotein containing approximately 20 percent (of its dry weight) of amino acids (Tyler, 1949; Vasseur, 1949b, 1950, 1952, 1954; Vasseur and Immers, 1949; Minganti and Vasseur, 1959). How the amino acids are arranged in the molecules is unknown. Indeed one might think of them as being scattered among the carbohydrate residues or clustered as peptides alternating with monosaccharide sequences. The fact that the jelly coat substance is split by proteolytic enzymes such as trypsin and chymotrypsin, which have specific requirements of peptide bonds, suggests that the latter alternative may be the right one. The carbohydrate components of the jelly coat substance of the eggs of various echinoderms are different in the different genera thus far investigated (Table 1). This has prompted the suggestion that this fact may be the chemical basis for the species-specificity of fertilization. Without ruling this out as *one* of the factors of specificity, we must remember that the relative distribution of monosaccharide residues and peptides in the molecules may give rise to a far greater variety of structure and hence to more subtle and specific differences.

It must finally be added that each carbohydrate residue is esterified with a $-SO_4$ group, and this, as mentioned before, gives the jelly coat substance its strongly acidic character (Vasseur, 1947).

THE AGGLUTINATION OF SPERMATOZOA

The most impressive effect of the jelly coat in solution is to cause an agglutination of the homologous spermatozoa (Fig. 2–3), and indeed the agglutinating titer is often used to indicate the concentration of "fertilizin" in solution. However, as will presently

Table 1
Chemical Composition of the Jelly Coat of Echinoderm Eggs
(Percent of Dry Weight)

Organism	G	Gl	M	F	X	Fr	N tot.	SO$_4$	Authors
Arbacia lixula	+	+	+	+					Minganti, 1958*
Echinus esculentus		+							Vasseur, 1950; Vasseur & Immers, 1949
Paracentrotus lividus	4.6		3.8	24.3	0.8		4.7	20.9	Minganti & Vasseur, 1959; Vasseur & Immers, 1949
Strongylocentrotus droebachiensis		+		+				25.0	Vasseur, 1947; Vasseur & Immers, 1949
Strongylocentrotus purpuratus	25						5.7	23	Tyler, 1948, 1949; Tyler & Fox, 1940
Sphaerechinus granularis	+		+	+					Minganti, 1958*
Heliocidaris crassispina				+					Nakano & Ohashi, 1954
Echinarachnius parma						+			Bishop, 1951; Bishop & Metz, 1952
Hemicentrotus pulcherrimus				+					Nakano & Ohashi, 1954
Pseudocentrotus depressus				+					Nakano & Ohashi, 1954
Echinocardium cordatum				32.7			4.1	20.5	Vasseur, 1952; Vasseur & Immers, 1949
Brissopsis lyrifera								8.1	Vasseur, 1952

+, qualitative estimation only; G, glucose; Gl, galactose; M, mannose; F, fucose; X, xylose; Fr, fructose; N tot., total nitrogen.
SOURCE: Minganti, 1958*

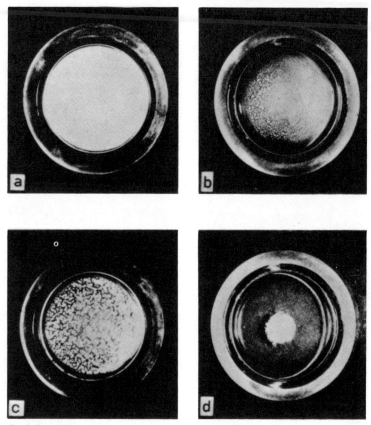

Fig. 2–3. Macroscopic appearance of agglutination in a dense suspension of sperm of *Megathura crenulata* (mollusk) induced by egg water: (a) before addition of egg water; (b), (c), and (d) 15 seconds, 30 seconds, and 10 minutes after addition of egg water. (From Tyler, 1941.)

be shown, agglutination has to be considered merely as a convenient means of exploring the nature of the interactions between jelly coat substance and spermatozoa, and indeed the analysis of this phenomenon has greatly contributed to our knowledge of the physiology of fertilization. In other words, agglutination is neither a physiological occurrence nor a reaction in any way involved in fertilization.

Nevertheless, the specific binding that occurs between jelly coat molecules and spermatozoa of the same species in the agglutination reaction strongly suggests that a similar interaction may take place while the spermatozoon approaches the egg and crosses the jelly coat to reach the egg surface. The importance of this phenomenon will become apparent from the following discussion.

However, let us first discuss some work aimed at clarifying the chemical nature of this interaction. The ability of jelly coat molecules in solution to agglutinate homologous spermatozoa indicates that each molecule must carry *not less* but probably more than two combining groups, thus making the binding with receptor groups at the surface of two or more spermatozoa possible. The spermatozoa are agglutinated by their heads; this indicates that the sperm receptors are located at the surface of the head. Tyler (1956) has calculated that the head of a sea urchin spermatozoon can easily accommodate 10^5 "fertilizin" molecules and this would cover only 10 percent of its surface. The clusters of agglutinated spermatozoa usually break up after a little while; now, however, the spermatozoa, although actively motile, have become unable to be re-agglutinated by fresh jelly coat solution and their fertilizing ability is strongly reduced. Let us consider these two important facts separately.

Jelly coat substance with labelled $-SO_4$ groups has been obtained by administering $Na_2S^{35}O_4$ to sea urchin females for several days during ovogenesis (Tyler and Hathaway, 1958). When a solution of such a radioactive jelly coat substance is saturated with spermatozoa, more than 70 percent of the radioactivity is removed due to the binding of the jelly coat molecules to the spermatozoa (Hathaway, 1959; Hathaway and Metz, 1961). This is consistent with an earlier report by Monroy *et al.* (1954), who showed that fucose, which is the main and typical carbohydrate component of the jelly coat of *Arbacia* (Minganti, 1958*) is removed from a jelly coat solution upon saturation with spermatozoa. Upon reversal of the agglutination, about one half of the radioactivity that was originally bound was released into the medium. This is probably due to the activity of a sulfatase located at the surface of the spermatozoa (Hathaway and Metz, 1961).

These experiments give clear evidence that in the reversal of the agglutination not only does a breakdown of the jelly coat molecules occur, but also one part of them remains attached to the spermatozoa while the other is set free. Hence the inability of the once agglutinated spermatozoa to be reagglutinated is due to the occupation of the receptor sites by the jelly coat fragments.

There are no data concerning the composition of the attached and released fragments.

It is pertinent to mention here that jelly coat solutions treated with proteolytic enzymes or with ultraviolet or x-radiations, or heated, lose their agglutinating power. Nevertheless spermatozoa treated with such nonagglutinating jelly coat solutions lose both their fertilizing power and their ability to be agglutinated by untreated jelly coat. Most probably, as a result of the treatments stated, the jelly coat molecules are split into small units (at the same site where they are split upon reversal of agglutination?), each one carrying just one combining group. Hence they can still attach to the surface of the spermatozoa but are unable to bring about agglutination. This has been called by Tyler (1941) "univalent fertilizin."

In starfish, jelly coat solutions fail to cause sperm agglutination. However, on the addition of an adjuvant (egg white, and also versene and other chelating agents) to the system, agglutination results (Metz, 1945). The effect of the adjuvants is explained as due to the removal of some ions which block surface groups of the spermatozoa and groups which are responsible for the binding to the complementary groups of the jelly coat molecules. In fact, treatment of the spermatozoa with the adjuvant, followed by washing with sea water, results in agglutination upon addition of jelly coat solution (see also Metz, 1957*).

The question has been raised (Monroy et al., 1954) as to the role played in fertilization by the jelly coat molecules which probably attach to the surface of the spermatozoon while it is going through the jelly coat; in particular, as to whether or not the spermatozoon enters the egg covered by its halo of jelly coat molecules. The evidence that will be presented in Chapter Three indicates that it does not, and indeed that the plasma membrane of the spermatozoon is left outside the egg. Although no clues are available for a satisfactory explanation, one might suggest that the reaction between the jelly coat and the sperm plasma membrane is necessary for the next step to take place, namely the peeling off of the plasma membrane from the head of the spermatozoon. This question will be discussed in the next chapter.

THE ACTIVATION OF SPERMATOZOA

The second main property attributed by Lillie to fertilizin was the activation of the spermatozoa. Activation of spermatozoa can most clearly be demonstrated when jelly coat solutions act on aged spermatozoa, which are almost immotile. Upon addition of a jelly coat solution, such spermatozoa show an outburst of motility. Furthermore, the treated spermatozoa stay motile much longer than untreated ones. This result is not easy to explain. One possibility is that the jelly coat in solution acts as a chelating agent; that is, it removes certain toxic ions from the sea water in just the same way that versene and some amino acids do (Tyler, 1950, 1953). It was first indicated by Gray (1928) that the oxygen consumption of spermatozoa treated with jelly coat solutions is increased. On the other hand, other investigations (Hayashi, 1946; Spikes, 1949; Rothschild, 1952) reached just the opposite conclusion: they observed a lowering of the oxygen consumption. The problem has been reinvestigated by Vasseur (1949a, 1954) who has produced evidence that the result depends largely on the condition of the spermatozoa: freshly shed spermatozoa give very little if any response, whereas aged ones do respond with an increased oxygen consumption. An important point to be kept well in mind is that spermatozoa are very delicate and easily damaged cells, and even slight changes of pH may influence their oxygen consumption (Rothschild, 1956).

The question can be asked now as to whether agglutination and activation are properties of the same or of different molecules. In other words, is the jelly coat substance made up of one or of two or more molecular types? We have already seen that the electrophoretic and ultracentrifugal analyses indicate one single component under the most varied pH ranges. Nevertheless, there is some indication that the jelly coat of the sea urchin egg may be inhomogeneous.

It had already been observed by Lillie (1913) that whereas the sperm-agglutinating power of fertilizin was lost in heating, the activator of sperm motility was not. This was confirmed by Tyler (1941) and by Vasseur (1949a). The activator proved also to be dialysable (Cornman, 1941; Vasseur and Hagström, 1946) and volatile (Clowes and Bachman, 1921). The question has recently been thoroughly studied by Hathaway (1963), who has presented convincing data that the respiratory activator, although contained in the jelly coat preparations, is probably a diffusion product of the egg itself. In fact it appeared in the sea water in which jellyless *Arbacia* eggs had been standing, and it was present in the diffusate of a dialysed homogenate of eggs. The activator proved to be alcohol soluble, heat stable and nonvolatile.

Messina and Monroy (1956), by chromatographic fractionation of *Arbacia* jelly coat on columns of a weakly anionic resin (Amberlite 1R-4B), obtained two fractions: the major fraction that is retained on the resin contains all the fucose and some galactose, whereas the one that is not retained (even after successive passages) contains only galactose. The amino acids are evenly (qualitatively) distributed among the two fractions. The interesting finding is that the agglutinating activity is almost entirely concentrated in the major fraction. Sperm activation was not tested. All this seems to point toward the presence in the jelly coat substance of at least two components that are both chemically and functionally distinct. Considering the important physiological role of the jelly coat in fertilization, it would certainly pay to undertake a thorough analysis of the jelly coat composition and molecular structure by using such methods as fingerprinting, amino acid sequence analysis, x-ray diffraction, etc. The results of such investigations are likely to yield important results also for the interpretation of the mode of action of the jelly coat.

EGG COATS IN ORGANISMS OTHER THAN ECHINODERMS

Although there are very few comparative studies, the glycoproteic or mucopolysaccharidic nature of the substances involved in the building up of the egg coats and responsible for the interaction between the gametes seems to be the rule.

In the algae the first step in the copulation of the gametes of opposite mating type is a flagellar agglutination; this is then followed by actual contact between the gamete bodies and formation of a protoplasmic bridge. The sex-specific agglutinines have been isolated, and at least in the case of the female agglutinine, extensively purified (Förster *et al.*, 1956). They are shown to be a sulfur-containing glycoprotein (a typical preparation had 5.86 percent N, 3.1 percent S, 2 pentose, 2 hexose and 12 amino acids). In its natural condition it appears to be in particulate form (molecular weight 100×10^6). Furthermore, both the female and the male agglutinines have been identified as the active surface components responsible for the mating type agglutination (Wiese and Jones, 1963).

In most amphibians the egg is surrounded by a thick jelly envelope. Its chemistry is fairly well known mainly due to the work of Hiyama (1949a, b, c) and Minganti and his collaborators (Minganti, 1954, 1955; Minganti and Azzolina, 1956; Minganti and D'Anna, 1957, 1958). This jelly coat is also a glycoprotein, but the main differences between it and the jelly coat of the echinoderm egg are its fairly high content of hexosamine (glucosamine and/or galactosamine) and its lack of sulfate (Table 2). Little or nothing is known of the physiology of the amphibian jelly coat. Bernstein (1952) had reported an agglutination of spermatozoa brought about by egg water of the mature eggs of *Rana clamitans;* however, Shaver *et al.* (1962) could not confirm this observation. It must be mentioned that the jelly coat of the amphibian egg in contact with water swells up and becomes impermeable to the spermatozoa. Fertilization in fact takes place *before* the eggs are laid or while they are being laid.

The situation in the ascidian eggs is quite interesting (Minganti, 1951). The egg water prepared from eggs with their membranes intact has a much lower sperm-agglutinating activity than that prepared from membraneless eggs. Hence the agglutinating substance must be present in a scarcely diffusible form, between the egg surface and the membrane.

The liquor folliculi of the mammalian egg has been found to be endowed with sperm-agglutinating ability (Corrias and Novarini, 1950). The agglutinating factor can be extracted with acidified water even from eggs which have lost their cells of the cumulus and of the corona, suggesting that its source is most likely the zona pellucida (Bishop and Tyler, 1956). There is evidence that the zona is a mucoprotein (Braden, 1952), with ester-bound sulfate groups (Seshachar and Bagga, 1963), and hence the analogy with the jelly coat of the echinoderm egg is very suggestive.

There are a few reports of agglutination and activation of spermatozoa induced by egg secretion in other vertebrates. The first one is due to Schartau and Montalenti (1941) and Montalenti and Schartau (1942), who described agglutination and activation of spermatozoa by egg water of *Lampetra fluviatilis.* However, in a

Table 2

Chemical Composition of the Jelly Coat of the Amphibian Eggs
(Percent of Dry Weight)

Organism	G	Gl	M	F	X	Ga	Gla	N tot.	Authors
Rana temporaria	?	12.7	3.5	7.1	?	8.9	9.5	8.1	Folkes, Grant & Jones, 1950
Rana esculenta	+	+		+	?	+	?	9.3	Giacosa, 1882; Minganti, 1955; Schulz & Becker, 1935
Rana japonica	?	28.0		?			14.0	8.8	Hiyama, 1949a, c
Rana clamitans	?	?	?	+			+		Bernstein, quoted by Minganti, 1958*
Discoglossus pictus	+	+	+	1.7			16.5	10.0	Minganti & D'Anna, 1958
Bufo bufo		+	+	10.4			20–40	7.6	Minganti, 1955; Minganti & Azzolina, 1956
Bufo vulgaris formosus		30.0		?			20.0	8.4	Hiyama, 1949a, b
Axolotl			+	+			+	8.3	Banta & Gartner, 1914; Minganti, 1955
Triturus cristatus		12.2	1.3	6.2			20.3	10.0	Minganti & D'Anna, 1957

+, qualitative estimation only; ?, to be controlled; G, glucose; Gl, galactose; M, mannose; F, fucose; X, xylose; Ga, glucosamine; Gla, galactosamine; N tot., total nitrogen.
SOURCE: Minganti, 1958*

later report Montalenti (1949) indicated that tap or distilled water also causes agglutination of spermatozoa, although less efficiently than egg water. He pointed out that agglutination by water is more evident in the dense than in the dilute suspension of spermatozoa. Also, herring spermatozoa are agglutinated in ordinary sea water and in Ringer (Yanagimachi, 1957a). The significance of this water-induced agglutination is difficult to visualize. It must be stressed again that spermatozoa are delicate cells and any rough treatment (such as centrifugation) is liable to damage them; this may result, as in the case of sea urchin spermatozoa, in a spontaneous agglutination. In other fishes (*Clupea pollasii,* Yanagimachi and Kanoh, 1953; Yanagimachi, 1957b, c; *Acheilognathus lanceolata, Acheilognathus taliva, Rhodeus ocellatus, Sarcocheilichys variegatus,* Suzuki, 1958, 1959a, b, 1960) agglutination of spermatozoa occurs at the micropyle, where they also seem to undergo activation. Hence in the teleostean eggs, only the micropyle seems to be endowed with the property of interacting with the spermatozoa; this property in other eggs is spread all over the egg surface.

CHEMOTAXIS

A question that needs to be discussed here, however briefly, is whether or not chemotaxis plays any role in the interaction between gametes. The question has been reviewed in detail by Rothschild (1956*), to whose book the interested reader is referred for more detailed information. As is known, the first to bring up the question of chemotaxis in fertilization was Pfeffer (1884), who not only showed chemotaxis in fern spermatozoa but indicated the α-malic acid as the substance responsible for this effect. That chemotaxis exists among plants is nowadays largely accepted, whereas among animals there is thus far no clear-cut example; an exception may be that of the egg of the medusan, *Spyrocodon saltatrix* (J. C. Dan, 1950b). Here the spermatozoa accumulate only at the pole of the egg where the nucleus lies close to the surface after the extrusion of the polar bodies. However, against the large body of negative evidence, this observation, although admittedly very suggestive, needs thorough examination and evaluation. One of the pitfalls in these experiments is that in a suspension of eggs and spermatozoa, when the latter collide with the highly viscous jelly coat of the eggs, they are trapped, so to speak, and get stuck to it. Hence, after a little while—and the phenomenon is more impressive in a dense suspension of spermatozoa—the eggs will be surrounded by a halo of spermatozoa. These may give the false impression of having been attracted, rather than trapped through purely casual collision.

In a recent paper Dickmann (1963) has presented some experimental results which should support the existence of chemotaxis in mammals. Rat and rabbit eggs were transferred into oviducts of newly mated rabbits and it was found that many more spermatozoa were attached to the zona of the rabbit egg than of the rat egg. Preliminary *in vitro* experiments had shown that rabbit spermatozoa when colliding with rat eggs become firmly attached to the zona. However, before any definite conclusion can be drawn, it would be important to find out about the comparative behavior of rabbit and rat spermatozoa towards rabbit eggs. The possibility of a particularly high "trapping" activity of the rabbit egg cannot a priori be ruled out.

In the case of the sea urchin gametes, the problem of chemotaxis was brought to the fore again by the work of Hartmann and his collaborators (Hartmann *et al.*, 1939; Hartmann and Schartau, 1939; Hartmann *et al.*, 1940). As a result of a number of experiments carried out mainly on the Mediterranean sea urchin *Arbacia lixula,* they suggested that the main fertilization substance in these eggs is the echinochrome. This is a substituted naphtho-quinone thoroughly studied by Kuhn's group (see Kuhn and Wallenfels 1940) which is responsible for the deep red color of the eggs and ovaries of the genus *Arbacia.* According to Hartmann *et al.* (1939), echinochrome itself exerts an activating and chemotactic effect on the sperm. According to the above-mentioned authors, echinochrome within the egg is bound to a high molecular substance, probably a protein, thus forming the so-called binary symplex, which has neither activating nor chemotactic activity on the spermatozoa. However, when passing to the outside of the egg, the binary symplex becomes bound to a further high-molecular compound, the material of the jelly coat. This ternary symplex is endowed with sperm-activating and sperm-agglutinating ability. However, the method used by the German authors to prepare the echinochrome in its various combinations is open to serious criticism (see Vasseur, 1954). The experiments and the theory of Hartmann and his colleagues have been further questioned by Tyler (1939b), Cornmann

(1941) and, more recently, Bielig and Dohrn (1950), who, under better controlled conditions, have not succeeded in repeating these experiments.

THE ACROSOME REACTION

As mentioned before, spermatozoa which have been agglutinated or have reacted with a jelly coat solution, undergo considerable reduction of their fertilizing ability, although remaining perfectly motile. It presently appears most likely that this is due to a modification induced in the acrosomal region of the spermatozoa, described as the *acrosome reaction*. The acrosome reaction has undoubtedly been one of the most significant of recent discoveries in the field of the physiology of fertilization. In spite of the variety of forms the acrosome reaction exhibits in the different animals, its end result is always the same, namely of establishing the first contact of the spermatozoon with the egg and of permitting the penetration of the egg. It is also assumed that the established contact with the egg is the initiator of the fertilization reaction. The first observation that the reaction with egg water causes a structural alteration in the acrosome was made by Popa (1927). He suggested that in this reaction some substance is squeezed off the acrosome. This observation was ignored for a long time and even considered with scepticism. Then, thanks to the work of J. C. Dan (Dan, 1952, 1954, 1956*, 1960; Dan and Wada, 1955) the importance of the acrosomal changes in fertilization was realized.

By the use of the electron microscope (summarized in 1956*), Dan observed that under certain conditions the spermatozoa of some animals (mainly those whose eggs are covered by a gelatinous coat, like the echinoderm) extrude a long thin filament (about 25 μ in the starfish). This appears to have been discharged from the acrosome and was therefore named *acrosomal* filament (Fig. 2–4). For a detailed discussion on the acrosome reaction the reader is referred to the reviews by J. C. Dan (1956*) and Colwin and Colwin (1964*). Only the essential points for the understanding of the process of the sperm-egg association will be mentioned here.

In *Hydroides* (Colwin and Colwin, 1961) and in *Saccoglossus* (Colwin and Colwin, 1963), for which we have the most detailed electron microscopic observations, the first step in the acrosome reaction is the dehiscence of the acrosomal vesicle, followed by the

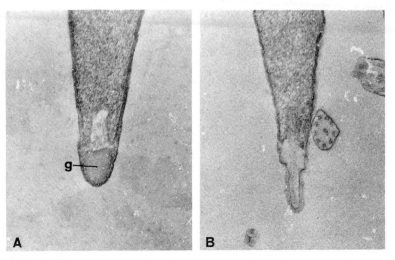

Fig. 2–4. Electron micrographs of spermatozoa of *Pseudocentrotus depressus,* showing a normal, unreacted spermatozoon (A) and a spermatozoon with fully formed acrosomal filament (B), following a 7-second exposure to jelly coat solution. Note, in (B), the disappearance of the acrosomal granule (*g*). (From J. C. Dan *et al.,* 1964.)

disappearance of the acrosomal granule (see Chapter Three and Figures 3–2, 3–7B, 3–9). In *Saccoglossus,* at the same time, a rapid deepening of a shallow invagination of the adnuclear part of the acrosomal membrane begins (Fig. 3–9A to C) and eventually results in the formation of the acrosomal tubule (Fig. 3–10). The elongation of the tubule is very rapid: in 7 seconds it has become nearly twice as long as the sperm head (see also Fig. 3–12A to E).

In *Hydroides,* the process is very similar: the only major difference is that instead of one single tubule, a bundle of about fifteen acrosomal tubules is formed (Figs. 3–3, 3–4, 3–7c to f).

As will be noted later, these tubular structures are instrumental in establishing the contact with the egg plasma membrane.

An acrosome is apparently lacking in the teleostean fishes. It is possible that, as suggested by Ginsburg (1963a), the presence of the micropylar canal, which enables the spermatozoa to reach the egg surface directly, may have brought about, in the course of evolution, the loss of the acrosome. It is indeed interesting that in the more primitive acipenserids a long acrosomal filament is still present in spite of the existence of a micropylar canal (Detlaff and Ginsburg, 1963).

In mammals, the spermatozoa become capable of fertilizing eggs only after staying a certain time in the female genital tract. It was thought that during this period the spermatozoa underwent a preparation of some kind that was called "capacitation." Now it has been shown that (at least in the golden hamster, in the Chinese hamster, in the guinea pig, and in the Libyan jird) capacitation consists of a progressive modification of the acrosomal region, and its final detachment from the sperm head, thus resulting in exposure of the perforatorium (Austin and Bishop, 1958a, b) (Fig. 2–5). On the other hand, no such change has been discerned in the rabbit spermatozoa in the Fallopian tube (Adams and Chang, 1962), whereas the acrosome appeared to have been lost in spermatozoa within the zona pellucida or in the perivitelline space (Austin, 1963) (Fig. 2–6). The analogy of capacitation with the acrosome reaction is quite impressive. (See addendum 2–1.)

The Colwins (1963) have proposed substituting the term "sperm activation" for "acrosomal reaction" to convey the idea of changes which in a sense are complementary to those of the egg activation. However, the writer feels that for descriptive purposes the older terminology is more appropriate. Furthermore, the expression "sperm activation" may cause some confusion with the activation, that is, the stimulation of motility and respiration, which in the sea urchin spermatozoa is brought about by jelly coat solutions.

Although the acrosome reaction may be caused by a great variety of different and unspecific agents, it seems very likely that the contact with the capsular material of the eggs enhances it under natural conditions. In the sea urchin, certainly the jelly coat in solution is a most potent acrosome-reaction-inducing agent. In the gastropods (J. C. Dan, 1956*), on the other hand, the reaction is not induced by the egg water but by direct contact with the jelly surrounding the egg. As soon as the spermatozoa come into contact with the jelly coat, they are seen to eject the filament. Most probably, what happens in nature is that when the spermatozoa touch the jelly coat, they immediately eject their acrosome. Now, although the acrosome filament is usually quite long, in the eggs covered by a jelly coat the best chances for it to reach the egg surface are when the spermatozoon hits the jelly radially. Evidently only some, and probably only a very few, of the spermatozoa colliding with

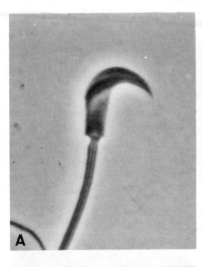
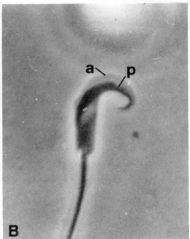
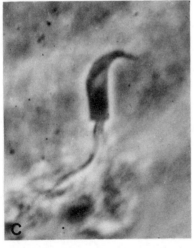

Fig. 2–5. Changes in the acrosomal region of the spermatozoon of the golden hamster as a result of capacitation: (A) Normal spermatozoon (from Austin and Bishop, 1958a). (B) A spermatozoon found moving actively through the cumulus oophorus; the acrosome is somewhat elevated and the perforatorium can be clearly seen; *a*, acrosome; *p*, perforatorium. (C) A sperm head found in the zona pellucida and showing lack of the acrosome. (B and C from Austin and Bishop, 1958b.)

the jelly will reach it headed in the right direction. The vast majority will deviate from such a direction. The chances that the acrosomal filament will reach the egg surface are smaller the greater its angle with the radial direction.

Now, if the acrosome reaction occurs prematurely, that is, before the spermatozoon has established contact with the jelly coat (a situation which may be caused by jelly coat in solution, or by other factors) the reacted spermatozoa may not be able to accom-

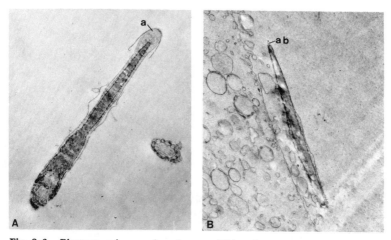

Fig. 2–6. Electron micrographs of an epididymal spermatozoon (A), and of a sperm head in the perivitelline space (B). Note in (B) the disappearance of the acrosome (*a*) and exposure of the apical body (*ab*), which in (A) is much less distinct, being masked by the content of the acrosome. (From Austin, 1963.)

plish successful fertilization. This may be the most important, if not *the* factor, which throws out of operation the agglutinated and reversed spermatozoa ("false fertilization," Bishop and Tyler, 1956). The saturation of the receptor sites at the surface of the agglutinated spermatozoa with jelly coat molecules may also play a role, although at present of a less definable nature, in disabling the agglutinated spermatozoa.

In other words, among the factors ensuring the success of fertilization, one of the most important is certainly the timely occurrence of the acrosome reaction.

ADDENDUM

2–1. The formation of a filament similar to the acrosomal filament has been seen in the pig spermatozoa within the zona (Dickmann and Dziuk, 1964).

DICKMANN, Z., and DZIUK, P. J., 1964. "Sperm penetration of the zona pellucida of the pig egg," *J. Exper. Biol.*, **41**: 603–608.

chapter three

The Penetration of the Spermatozoon

The process of penetration of the spermatozoon into the egg may be subdivided into at least three steps: (1) the passage of the spermatozoon through the coats and/or membranes surrounding the egg; (2) the establishment of specific contact between the spermatozoon and the egg plasma membrane; and (3) its actual incorporation into the egg.

THE PENETRATION OF THE SPERMATOZOON THROUGH THE EGG COATS

In some eggs, such as those of the fishes, the membrane is pierced by the micropylar canal (Fig. 3–1). In all other eggs covered either by a jelly coat or even more by thick and often tough vitelline membranes, there can scarcely be any doubt that the spermatozoon must be able to "make a hole" in the membrane(s) to reach the egg.

The problem of the egg membrane lysin has been extensively investigated in mammals, and indeed, an enzyme considered responsible for the dissolution of the egg coats has been obtained from sperm. It had been observed long ago by Yamane (1930, 1935) and Pincus and Enzmann (1932) that the cells of the cumulus oophorus are rapidly dispersed upon contact with spermatozoa. Since at that time it was not known that these cells are held together by a mucopolysaccharide rich in hyaluronic acid, it was thought that a proteolytic activity was involved (Yamane, 1930). It was not until 1942 that Fekete and Duran Reynals and MacLean and Rowlands were able to show that the enzyme hyaluronidase, which is present in high concentrations associated with the sperm fraction of semen, is able to cause the dispersion of the cumulus cells. As mentioned before, the zona pellucida is made up of a mucoprotein (Braden, 1952), but not much is known about its exact composition and

24

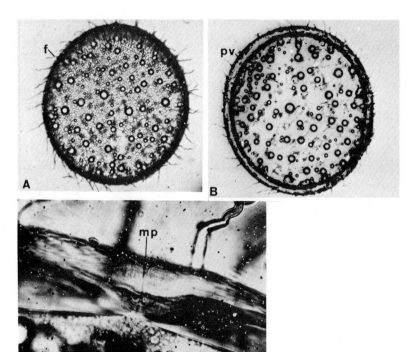

Fig. 3–1. (A) Unfertilized and (B) fertilized egg of *Oryzias latipes,* 4 minutes after addition of sperm (insemination); *f,* chorionic filaments. Before fertilization the egg surface is in close contact with the chorion. The perivitelline space (*pv*) forms after fertilization as a result of a shrinkage of the egg, which is accompanied by the squeezing out of the perivitelline fluid. Note the disappearance of cortical alveoli in the fertilized egg (compare with Fig. 4–5). (C) The micropylar canal (*mp*) in the chorion of the unfertilized egg. (Courtesy of Dr. E. Nakano.)

therefore nothing can be inferred as to the possible mechanism by which the spermatozoa pass through it. Although the zona does not seem to be altered by hyaluronidase, this enzyme has been reported to abolish the metachromasia of the zona of cat oocytes (Konecny, 1959). Proteolytic enzymes—especially trypsin—are effective in dissolving the zona (see Austin, 1961*). Hence there is the possibility that dispersion of the cumulus cells and breaching of the zona may be caused by two different enzymes, the former by the hyaluronidase, the latter perhaps by a protease. Narrow slits can be observed in the zona pellucida following the passage of the spermatozoa; this certainly suggests an enzymatic attack on the part of the spermatozoa, but thus far all attempts to extract a zona lysin from spermatozoa have been unsuccessful. For more detailed information about the mammalian egg, the reader is referred to Austin's book (1961*).

The suggestion that, as in mammals, the sea urchin spermatozoon enzymically depolymerises the jelly coat and thus opens up its way to the egg, was presented by Monroy and Ruffo (1947). However, Krauss (1950a, b, c) was unable to repeat their results. The question was reinvestigated by Monroy and Tosi (1952) and by Monroy *et al.* (1954), who arrived at the conclusion that the viscosity-lowering effect of live spermatozoa on jelly coat solutions *in vitro* (see also Vasseur, 1951) is mainly due to the binding of jelly coat molecules to the surface of the spermatozoa as described in Chapter Two. There seems to be no reason to doubt that a similar attachment may also occur *in vivo*, but it is difficult to say whether or not it is of any importance in the passage of the spermatozoon through the jelly coat.

Messina (1954) has actually produced some evidence that a depolymerization of the jelly coat of an enzymatic type occurs under the action of spermatozoa. In the sea urchin *Mellita quinquiesperforata*, Brookbank (1958) has given evidence of a jelly coat dispersing factor located at the surface of the spermatozoa. The presence of a sulfatase at the surface of the spermatozoa has also been suggested (Hathaway and Metz, 1961). It would certainly be interesting to learn more about this enzyme and its role, if any, in the passage of the spermatozoon through the jelly coat.

A purely physical mechanism has been suggested by J. C. Dan, at least for the eggs covered only by a gelatinous coat. The acrosomal filament may pierce the jelly coat "with the push derived from the chemical change which causes its formation" (Dan, 1960). This, however, does not rule out that the acrosomal reaction involves also the release of an egg membrane lysin. Indeed there is evidence (see below) that this may actually be so.

A powerful lysin must be involved in the passage of the spermatozoon through the membrane of some eggs, such as those of polychaetes. If eggs of *Pomatoceros* are transferred to dilute sea water within five minutes after fertilization, in most of them (about 74 percent) there occurs an outflow of cytoplasm from one point of the membrane. This indicates that when entering the egg the spermatozoon does make a real hole in the vitelline membrane. It is worth mentioning that a healing of the holes of the membrane seems also to take place. Indeed, if the eggs are transferred to hypotonic sea water at time intervals after fertilization, it can be seen that within 30 minutes 50 percent of the eggs no longer show any cytoplasmic outflow (Monroy, 1948b).

We are indebted to the work of Colwin *et al.* (1957) and of Colwin and Colwin (1961) for the most detailed information about the process whereby the spermatozoon goes through the vitelline membrane of the egg of another polychaete, *Hydroides*. Following contact with the vitelline membrane, the apex of the acrosome breaks open and the acrosomal membrane and the plasma membrane of the sperm head fuse all along the orifice (Figs. 3–2 and 3–7B). Then at the point of contact with the tip of the acrosome, the vitelline membrane appears ruptured; at the same time, the acrosomal granule gradually fades away. Also in the middle layer of the membrane, that is, in the thick layer interposed between the outer layer of the membrane and the egg plasma membrane, a clear area forms all around the acrosome. This area is interpreted as an indication of lysis. Also in the fertilization of the egg of *Saccoglossus* (enteropneust) (Colwin and Colwin, 1963) the contact of the spermatozoon with the egg envelopes is immediately followed by the dehiscence of the acrosomal vesicle and the disappearance of the acrosomal granule (Figs. 3–9 and 3–12A, B). At the point of contact with the spermatozoon, a pit forms in the egg envelope.

These observations also suggest that the dissolution of the acrosomal granule may be instrumental in releasing a membrane lysin. Actually Tyler must be credited for having presented the first evidence of the acrosomal location of the sperm lysin (1949). He found that the acrosomal region of spermatozoa of the mollusk *Megathura crenulata*, when submitted to treatment effective in extracting the lysin, appears ruptured.

An interesting observation has been made by Wada, Collier and Dan (1956). They were able to recover the lysin *from the sea water* in which *Mytilus* spermatozoa had been standing, but only

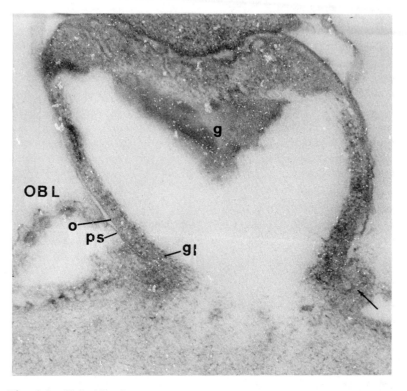

Fig. 3–2. *Hydroides hexagonus.* A spermatozoon that has established contact with the egg membrane. The tip of the acrosomal vesicle is now open, and in the contact area the outer border layer (*OBL*) of the vitelline membrane has been breached. Note the beginning of eversion (arrow) of the outer zone (*o*) of the acrosomal wall, together with its granular layer (*gl*); the acrosomal granule (*g*) has started to decrease in size. Note *ps*, the plasma membrane of the spermatozoon. This stage corresponds to stage (b) of Fig. 3–6. (From Colwin and Colwin, 1961.)

if the latter were in the "reacted" condition (that is, if they had an ejected acrosomal filament).

On the other hand, if the acrosomal reaction had not taken place, then the lysin could be *extracted from the spermatozoa.* This is certainly quite an important result, as it might help to explain a number of conflicting results as to the existence and location of the lysins.

Also, in the mammals it has been suggested that the perforatorium may be the carrier of the "zona lysin" (Austin and Bishop, 1958a, b). In fact, as has been described in Chapter Two, the significance of the "capacitation" may actually be that of exposing the perforatorium that, due to its lysin, would allow the spermatozoon to go through the egg membranes and in particular through the zona. (See addendum 3–1.)

Therefore, one aspect of the acrosomal reaction may be that of exposing the lysin-containing acrosomal component; a strong and localized action of the lysin on the egg envelope would thus be ensured.

Numerous attempts have been made to extract the lysin or lysins from the spermatozoa and define them chemically. However, except for the mammals, the information available is still very limited.

Tyler (1939) succeeded in extracting a powerful egg membrane lysin from the sperm of *Megathura* submitted to freezing and thawing. The preparation quickly dissolved the thick membrane of the egg of this mollusk.

This procedure was also effective in extracting the jelly coat dispersing factor from the sperm of *Mellita* (Brookbank, 1958) and the membrane lysin from the sperm of *Hydroides* (Colwin and Colwin, 1958, 1960). The *Hydroides* lysin promptly dissolved the thick middle layer of the membrane of the egg. However, the lysin apparently left intact the thin outer and inner border layer of the membrane. This suggests that the rupturing of the outer layer of the membrane and the liquefaction of the middle layer are brought about by two different factors: the former is either more tightly bound to the structure of the spermatozoon or more labile and hence destroyed by the extraction procedure.

Very little can be said about the chemistry of these lysins; the main difficulty lies in the very small amounts obtained, which are insufficient for proper purification and analysis. Nevertheless a fairly high degree of purification has been achieved with the lysin from *Mytilus* sperm (Hauschka, 1963). The properties of the lysin prepared from the sperm of *Megathura* (Tyler, 1939; Krauss, 1950 a and b), *Mytilus* (Berg, 1950; Hauschka, 1963) and *Hydroides* (Colwin and Colwin, 1958) indicate that they are proteins. However it is not known to which class of enzymes they belong. The membrane lysin of *Pomatoceros* is inhibited by oxidized gluta-thione; this has been taken as an indication that it might possibly be a proteolytic enzyme (Monroy, 1948 b).

Experiments to test the species-specificity of the membrane lytic agents have been carried out on several species of mollusks (Tyler, 1939a; von Medem, 1942, 1945; Berg, 1950), and a high degree of specificity has been ascertained. On the other hand, a lysin extracted from sea urchin sperm has been found effective in dissolving the egg membrane of the mollusk *Megathura crenulata* (Krauss, 1950c).

THE PENETRATION OF THE SPERMATOZOON INTO THE EGG

Let us now turn to the problem of the process of actual sperm penetration into the egg. The case of the *Asterias* egg must be mentioned first, also for historical reasons: indeed, it was on this egg that the classical observations of Fol (1879) were made. Fol

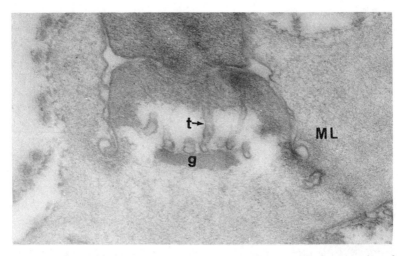

Fig. 3-3. *Hydroides hexagonus.* The acrosome is now largely everted and lies deeply in the middle layer (*ML*) of the vitelline membrane. The acro-somal granule (*g*) is considerably reduced while the tubules (*t*) have started to elongate. Corresponds to stage (c) of Fig. 3-6. (From Colwin and Colwin, 1961.)

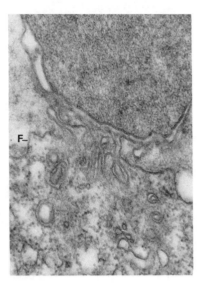

Fig. 3–4. *Hydroides hexagonus.* Contact between spermatozoon and egg is established by means of elongated acrosomal tubules indenting egg plasma membrane. Here *F* indicates the wall of the fertilization cone. Corresponds to stages (a) and (b) of Fig. 3–7. (From Colwin and Colwin, 1961.)

observed that the first contact between the spermatozoon and the egg was established by means of a very thin filament extending through the jelly and connecting the head of the spermatozoon to the surface of the egg. He further observed that while the spermatozoon moved through the jelly layer, the egg sent out a hyaline protrusion which extended towards the spermatozoon with amoeboid movements. The "fertilization cone" then thus appeared to meet and engulf the spermatozoon and eventually carry it inside the egg.

Fol also considered the possibility that the progress of the spermatozoon towards the egg might be due to the retraction of the connecting filament. The presence of this "insemination filament" was later confirmed by Chambers (1930), who observed that ". . . suddenly within an instant, a distinct line could be seen connecting its tip [the tip of the fertilization cone] with the head of a spermatozoon." He also noticed that ". . . the insemination filament always connects with a spermatozoon" and he was inclined to agree with Fol as to the role of the filament in pulling the spermatozoon towards the egg. Both Fol and Chambers, however, dismissed the idea that the filament might arise from the spermatozoon.

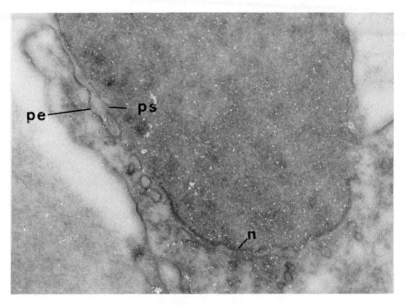

Fig. 3–5. *Hydroides hexagonus.* Spermatozoon entering egg cytoplasm. Note continuity of egg plasma membrane (*pe*) and the plasma membrane of the spermatozoon (*ps*); *n,* apical part of the nuclear envelope. Corresponds to stage (c) of Fig. 3–7. (From Colwin and Colwin, 1961.)

The role of the fertilization cone in pulling the spermatozoon towards the egg became doubtful when it was observed that in several marine eggs (for example, *Echinarachnius, Arbacia,* and *Paracentrotus,* Chambers, 1933) the cone forms *after* the spermatozoon has sunk into the egg.

Following the discovery of the acrosome reaction, it became clear that the insemination filament is actually the acrosome filament; the Colwins (1955, 1956) could see quite clearly (in *Thyone, Holothuria* and *Asterias*) that the fertilization cone creeps up the filament to join the sperm head. Whether or not in these eggs the filament actually pulls the spermatozoon is hard to say. Anyway, according to the Colwins, in some echinoderm eggs the filament remains visible fully extended within the egg for some time.

Also, in *Saccoglossus* the fibrous core of the acrosomal tubule may be seen within the cytoplasm of newly fertilized eggs, but it is hard to judge whether or not it has somehow shortened.

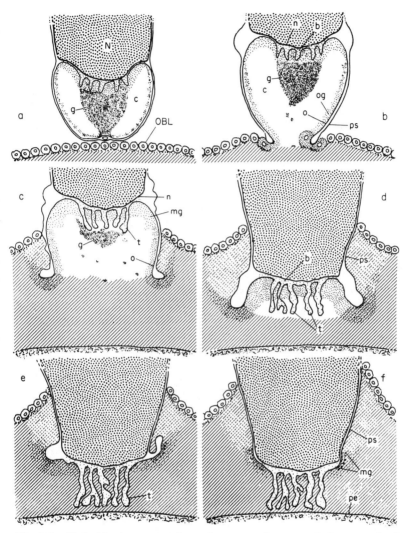

Fig. 3–6. *Hydroides hexagonus.* Successive stages of passage of the sperm head into the vitelline membrane: (a) presumed position at time of contact; (b) breaching of the outer border layer (*OBL*) of the vitelline membrane and beginning of eversion of outer and intermediate zone of the acrosomal wall; (c) progress of the eversion of the acrosomal wall, disappearance of the acrosomal granule and beginning of elongation of acrosomal tubules while the intermediate layer of vitelline membrane is breached. In (d) to (f), the elongating acrosomal tubules have almost reached the egg plasma membrane. Within the diagrams: *b*, material lying between nuclear envelope and base of acrosome; *c*, cavity of acrosomal vesicle; *g*, acrosomal granule; *N*, nucleus of the sperma-

The most detailed information concerning the process of sperm penetration into an egg has been provided by the work of the Colwins on the fertilization of the eggs of *Hydroides* (1961) and *Saccoglossus* (1963). In *Saccoglossus*, the long acrosomal tubule (formed as described in Chapter two) reaches the egg plasma membrane and fuses with it; at the point of contact the two plasma membranes, that of the spermatozoon and that of the egg, fuse (Figs. 3–11C to E and 3–12A, B). Thus a kind of funnel is formed through which the egg nucleus moves. In doing so it adapts itself to the narrow passage and becomes cigar shaped (Figs. 3–10 and 3–12C to F). When the contact between the tip of the acrosomal tubule and the egg plasma membrane is established, the egg surface protrudes in the form of a cone; this is the well known fertilization cone (Fig. 3–12A to F). Once the fusion of the plasma membranes of the two gametes is established, the egg cytoplasm (of the cone) begins to intrude between the sperm nucleus and the sperm plasma membrane (Figs. 3–12D, E and 3–10). Thus while the sperm nucleus moves inside the egg it is progressively denuded of its membrane. The peeling process involves all the structures of the sperm head, in particular the middle piece and the centriole (Fig. 3–12F).

The process of sperm penetration is substantially similar in *Hydroides,* in which, however, the acrosome, instead of forming one single tubule, forms a bundle of acrosomal tubules (Figs. 3–3; 3–4; 3–6c to f). The surface of the *Hydroides* egg projects in microvilli which extend within the vitelline membrane. The acrosomal tubules will hence encounter the microvilli during their growth process, but there is evidence that extended contact with the egg surface occurs *at the base* and not at the tip of the microvilli. At the point of contact the further elongation of the acrosomal tubules causes an indentation of the egg surface (Figs. 3–4; 3–7a, b). Nevertheless, no fusion occurs between the egg plasma membrane and the membrane of the tubules. A fertilization cone has meanwhile started to form and to surround the sperm head; at the point of contact, a fusion between the egg and the sperm plasma membrane

Fig. 3–6 (cont'd). tozoon; *n,* nuclear envelope; *o;* outer zone of the acrosomal membrane; *og,* granular layer of outer zone; *mg,* granular layer of the intermediate zone; *pe,* plasma membrane of the egg; *ps,* plasma membrane of the spermatozoon; *t,* acrosomal tubules. (From Colwin and Colwin, 1961.)

occurs (Figs. 3-5 and 3-7c). From now on the process almost duplicates that of Saccoglossus; that is, the egg cytoplasm intrudes between the sperm plasma membrane and the egg nucleus (Figs. 3-7d). Since the fusion of the plasma membranes occurs over a far wider area than in Saccoglossus, no change of shape of the nucleus occurs while it is being incorporated in the egg (Fig. 3-7d to f).

In the fertilization of the sea urchin the processes seem to be fundamentally similar to those described thus far (Fig. 3-13).

The denudation of the head of the spermatozoon while entering the egg has also been observed in the rat (Szollosi and Ris, 1961), in the rabbit (Hadék, 1963a), and in the mollusk Barnea candida (Pasteels and de Harven, 1962). It is interesting to note that a fusion of the membrane of one of the sperm flagella with the egg membrane has also been found to be the first step in the fertilization of the green alga, Prasiola stipitata (Friedmann, 1962). (See addenum 3-2.)

It seems thus that the establishment of a specific contact, then followed by the fusion of the plasma membranes of the two gametes, is the first fundamental step in the penetration of the spermatozoon into the egg. But it is also of interest that the sperm plasma membrane appears to have no other function in fertilization besides that of establishing such a contact; indeed, once this has been achieved, the membrane must be left outside the egg. *Only a naked nucleus is admitted within the egg and can participate in the formation of the zygote.*

This may be the reason why live spermatozoa injected with a micropipette into a sea urchin egg have not only failed to activate the egg but have even failed to show any one of the changes the sperm nucleus normally undergoes within the fertilized egg (Hiramoto, 1962a). Also spermatozoa entering an egg through a damaged cortex fail to form an aster (Runnström and Kriszat, 1952). It may be pertinent to recall here that nonprimate cells, normally unsusceptible to polio virus infection, can be successfully infected by the isolated virus RNA and give rise to normal, complete virus particles (McLaren, Holland and Syverton, 1959; Holland and McLaren, 1959; Holland, McLaren and Syverton, 1959a, b).

An interesting observation has been made by Pasteels (1963) who has found that in Barnea, immediately after the formation of the second polar body, the naked sperm nucleus, which until then

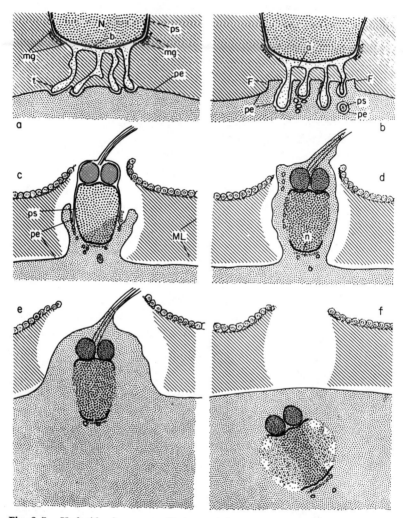

Fig. 3-7. *Hydroides hexagonus.* Fusion and incorporation of spermatozoon and egg: (a) and (b) Acrosomal tubules of sperm head indent, but egg plasma membrane still intervenes between egg cytoplasm and sperm plasma membrane of tubules. (c) Fusion of egg plasma membrane with sperm plasma membrane, with vesiculation near presumed site of fusion. (d) Within their common plasma membrane, egg cytoplasm surrounds sperm structures. (e) and (f) Sperm structures penetrate more deeply into egg cytoplasm; mitochondrial and apical parts of nuclear envelope remain still visible but peripheral part of nucleus becomes diffuse; fertilization cone recedes (in f). *ML,* middle layer of the vitelline membrane; other symbols as in Fig. 3-6. (From Colwin and Colwin, 1961.)

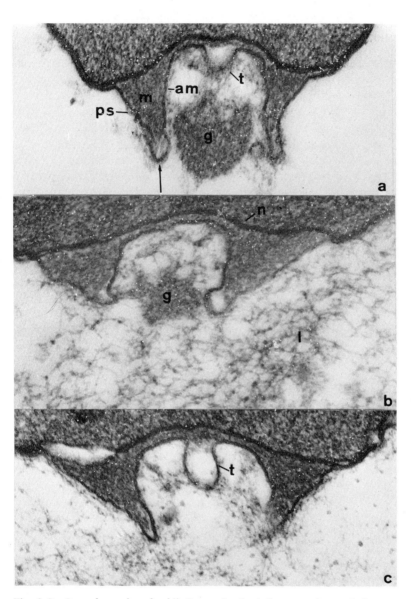

Fig. 3–8. *Saccoglossus kowalevskii.* Sperm head at the outer layer of the egg envelope (*I*) showing dehiscence of the acrosomal vesicle. Note (arrow) junction of plasma (*ps*) and acrosomal membrane (*am*). (a) Release of the acrosomal granule (*g*), which in (c) (a slightly later stage) has practically disappeared; (b) A lateral section of a stage nearly identical to (a), showing

37

had remained unchanged underneath the egg surface, is rapidly covered by a new membrane built up by the endoplasmic reticulum of the egg.

The middle piece of the spermatozoon is consistently carried inside the egg together with the head material. Whether or not it plays any role is doubtful; actually the morphological evidence speaks against it. In fact, Meves (1912, 1914) observed that in the sea urchin egg the middle piece remains quite unchanged through the fifth cleavage and appears to be passively dragged into one or the other of the blastomeres. Similar observations have been made by J. C. Dan (1950a). It may be mentioned in passing that since the middle piece is known to contain the mitochondrial apparatus of the spermatozoon, these observations make it unlikely that the sperm mitochondria play any role in the metabolic changes of the egg at the time of fertilization.

THE NATURE OF THE INTERACTION BETWEEN SPERMATOZOON AND EGG PLASMA MEMBRANE

From the description given in the preceding paragraph, it is clear that the process of sperm penetration requires establishment of a highly specific interaction between the plasma membranes of the two gametes.

As visualized by Tyler (summarized in 1956, 1959, and 1960), the first step in this process is a specific interaction between specific complementary receptor groups that are in apposition on the sperm and egg surfaces. This interaction causes the egg surface, that is, the part of the egg surface protruding through the vitelline membrane in the form of microvilli, to expand progressively over the sperm head, eventually engulfing it completely. The observations of the Colwins described above indicate that the sperm head is not actually engulfed. The fusion of the plasma membranes of the

---

Fig. 3–8 (*cont'd*). the frayed edge of the acrosomal granule. In (a) invagination of the adnuclear part of the acrosomal membrane (*t*) has just begun to deepen. (c) Invagination is deeper and will soon become the acrosomal tubule. (Compare with stages (A) to (C) in Fig. 3–11). *n*, nuclear envelope. (From Colwin and Colwin, 1963.)

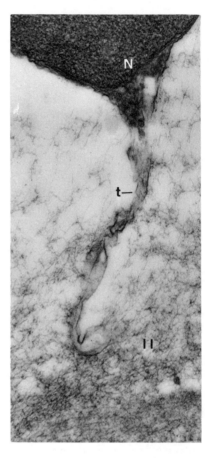

Fig. 3–9. *Saccoglossus kowalevskii.* Fully extended acrosomal tubule (*t*) now in contact with inner egg envelope (*II*). The nucleus (*N*) has started to protrude at the base of the tubule. Note that the wall of the tubule is the sperm plasma membrane. Fibrous core of the tubule is also visible. (Compare with Figs. 3–11E and 3–12A to C). (From Colwin and Colwin, 1963.)

two gametes results indeed in the formation of a funnel through which the contents of the head of the spermatozoon moves into the egg cytoplasm. An interaction between specific complementary groups at the surface of the two gametes may be a prerequisite for such a membrane fusion.

This is the more evident now that we know that the fusion of the two gametes implies a *fusion* of their plasma membranes which cannot occur short of a structural similarity at the molecular level.

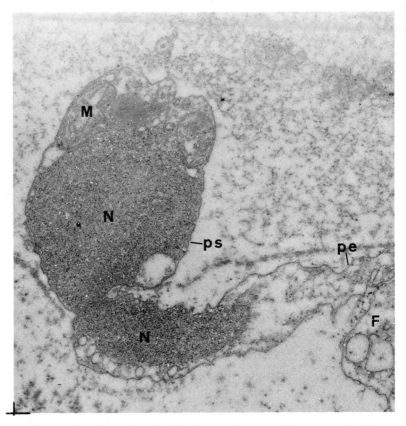

Fig. 3–10. *Saccoglossus kowalevskii.* Apex of sperm nucleus surrounded by egg cytoplasm in fertilization cone (*F*) (to be compared with stages (D) and (E) of Fig. 3–12.) Note constricted profile of nucleus (*N*) and continuity of plasma membrane of spermatozoon (*ps*) and of egg (*pe*). *M*, mitochondrion. (From Colwin and Colwin, 1963.)

Further important information has been provided by the serological analysis of the specific antigenic groups at the surface of the two gametes.

A study of the antigens at the surface of the spermatozoa has been undertaken by Metz and his collaborators. It was known that fertilization can be inhibited by treatment of sperm with antisperm sera (Tyler, 1946; Metz, 1962). In the *Arbacia* sperm, at least three surface antigens (defined as those antigens which can be detected

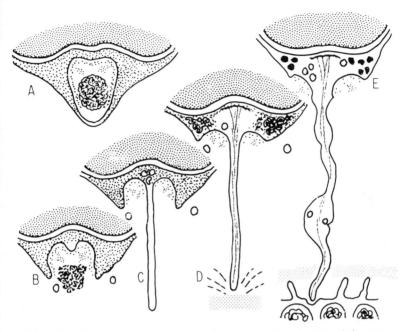

Fig. 3–11. Diagrams illustrating successive stages of the changes of the acrosomal region of *Saccoglossus* spermatozoon at the beginning of fertilization. (A) normal appearance of the unreacted acrosome; (B) to (E) stages from dehiscence of acrosomal vesicle and disappearance of the granule to the formation and elongation of acrosomal tubule, reaching, in (E), almost to the egg plasma membrane. (From Colwin and Colwin, 1963.)

by the sperm-agglutinating action of antisera) can be detected. One of these is shared with the spermatozoa of *Lytechinus variegatus* and *Echinarachnius parma*, another only with the former, and the third is specific for *Arbacia* spermatozoa (Köhler and Metz, 1960). By a variety of immunological tests it has further been shown that in the *Arbacia* spermatozoa the essential antigen in fertilization is the one shared with *Lytechinus* only. In fact anti-*Arbacia* sperm serum digested with papain (in order to make it univalent and thus avoid agglutination), which completely inhibits the fertilizing power of *Arbacia* spermatozoa, fails to do so when absorbed with *Lytechinus* spermatozoa (Metz, Schuel and Bischoff, 1964). Investigations into the surface antigens of the egg have been carried out by Perlmann (summarized in 1959). According to this author, at least four dif-

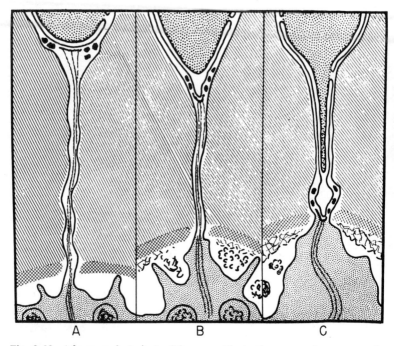

A   B   C

Fig. 3–12 (*above and facing*). Diagrams illustrating successive stages of zygote formation in *Saccoglossus*. Following the fusion of the plasma membranes of the two gametes, in (A), the nucleus progressively enters the egg cytoplasm, being constricted in the narrow tubule (C to E). At the same time, the egg cytoplasm intrudes between the structures of the sperm head and the zygote plasma membrane (in that part that formerly was sperm plasma membrane and now has become continuous with the egg plasma membrane in the fertilization cone). Note the fibrous core of the acrosomal tubule within the egg cytoplasm. (F) Recession of the fertilization cone and swelling of the sperm nucleus. (From Colwin and Colwin, 1963.)

ferent antigens are present at or near the surface of the unfertilized sea urchin egg. Two of them, the J-antigen, which is present mainly in the jelly coat, and the C-antigen, which is responsible for the cortical damage caused by treatment with some antisera, are of a rather obscure significance. The most interesting ones are the A- and F-antigens. The former, whose determinant groups are largely carbohydrates, is indicated by Perlmann as the activation antigen. In fact activation was reported to occur in the eggs exposed to an antiserum containing anti-A antibodies. However, several attempts

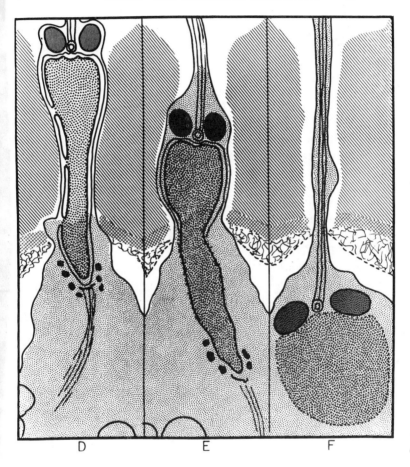

Fig. 3–12.

to repeat this observation—which if confirmed would be of great importance—have thus far failed (Tyler, 1959; Tyler *et al.*, 1961). Finally, the F-antigen is considered "a specific sperm receptor of the egg surface." In fact, the result of treatment with an antiserum containing the F-antibodies is a depression of the fertilization rate.

The presence of specific receptor sites in the jelly of *Rana pipiens* is indicated by the inhibition of fertilizability of these eggs when treated with nonprecipitating (papain-digested) antijelly sera (Shivers and Metz, 1962).

Further investigations along this promising line would be of the utmost importance, as they might eventually identify the mechanism of the specific interaction between sperm and egg. It is anticipated that the use of univalent, nonprecipitating, antibodies will be of great value in these studies.

The location of the specific reacting groups at the surface of the egg, that is, whether on the vitelline membrane or on the plasma membrane or on both, is not known. The presence of such groups on the plasma membrane is suggested by the refertilization experiments which will be discussed later. They show that in some sea urchin species fertilized eggs can be entered by additional spermatozoa following removal or chemical alteration of the fertilization membrane. The evidence about the presence of reacting groups on the vitelline membrane is inconclusive. In fact the polyspermy which follows the treatment of the eggs with proteolytic enzymes (which inhibits the elevation of the fertilization membrane) may depend on an alteration of the egg cell (plasma) membrane rather than of the vitelline membrane (see Chapter Four). The situation may be different in other eggs: for example, the protection against self-fertilization and heterofertilization which in the ascidian egg is afforded by the chorionic membrane (Chapter Four) may be indicative of the presence on the membrane of specific groups.

ADDENDUM

3–1. Drs. Hartree and Srivastava, Cambridge, England, have kindly informed the author that they have now succeeded in isolating the acrosome from ram, bull, and rabbit spermatozoa. An extract of the isolated acrosomes proved effective in dispersing the corona radiata and dissolving the zona of rabbit eggs.

3–2. According to the description of the Colwins, the sperm plasma membrane, being left outside the egg, remains as a kind of extraneous patch incorporated into the egg plasma membrane. Recent work by Tyler (1964 and personal communication) suggests that this may not be so. Tyler's electron micrographs (of *Urechis* and *Lytechinus* eggs) show that the two plasma membranes, that of the egg and that of the spermatozoon, establish a lateral joining followed by a very rapid breakdown of the conjoined membranes.

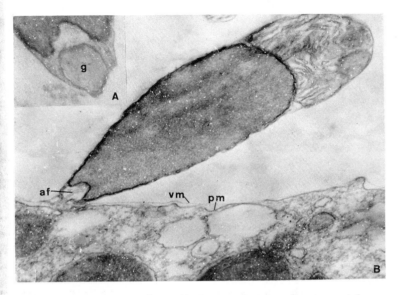

Fig. 3–13. *Arbacia punctulata.* (A) Acrosomal region of an unreacted spermatozoon: note the large acrosomal granule (*g*). *(B)* An egg a few seconds after sperm attachment. The section shows the opening of the acrosomal vesicle and the disappearance of the granule. Note the formation of the acrosomal filament *(af)*. The vitelline membrane *(vm)* has just separated from the egg plasma membrane *(pm)*. (Courtesy of Dr. L. Franklin.)

This interpretation would also account for the otherwise unexplained linear arrangement of vesicles in the egg cytoplasm just in contact with the region of junction of the egg and sperm plasma membranes (seen very clearly in figure 12 of A. L. Colwin and L. H. Colwin, 1961). Thus, while the sperm head is being incorporated into the egg cytoplasm, the sperm plasma membrane is progressively broken down. At the end of the process, the original integrity and continuity of the egg plasma membrane would thus be reestablished. According to recent studies by Piko and Tyler (1964) a similar process of engulfment by lateral apposition and subsequent breakdown of egg and sperm plasma membranes occurs in the rat.

Piko, L., and Tyler, A., 1964. "Fine Structural studies of sperm penetration in the rat," *Proc. Vth Intern. Congr. Animal Reprod.*, Trento, 2: 372–377.

Tyler, A., 1964. "Studies on fertilization and early development," *Engineering and Science Magazine*, 27: 17–20.

chapter four

The Egg Cell Membrane: Its Structural and Physiological Changes at Fertilization

The cell membrane has always attracted a great deal of attention. All the traffic to and from the cell passes across this membrane; an important role in the regulation of cell metabolism has therefore rightly been attributed to it. Besides this, the membrane of each cell type has some specialized function. The specialization of the cell membrane of the egg is its ability to react with the spermatozoon (see Chapter Three). Therefore it seems pertinent at this point to discuss what is known about the egg cell membrane and the changes it undergoes upon fertilization.

GENERAL CONSIDERATIONS

The widely accepted model proposed by Danielli (summarized in 1942) postulates a common structural plan for all cell membranes. According to this model, all cell membranes are lipoprotein structures in which a double layer of oriented lipid chains is interposed between two protein leaflets. In the lipid double layer, the orientation of the lipid molecules depends on their having a polar end which is oriented toward the aqueous phase—that is, towards the protein layer—and a hydrocarbon end which is oriented toward the hydrocarbon end of another lipid molecule. For any model of the cell membrane to be acceptable, it must be able to account for selective permeability, a property on which the life of any cell depends. Recent work has led the physiologists to postulate the presence in the membrane of the nerve fiber of pores about 4.5 A wide, lined with negative charges which repel anions while allowing cations to pass through (see Mullins, 1960). The presence of pores does not account for all the permeability properties of the membrane, and indeed we now know that the cells develop special active transport mechanisms which enable them to take in those molecules which because of their size would not be able to pass the membrane by a simple diffusion mechanism. Furthermore, the cells possess selective mechanisms which allow them to discriminate among ions. The most important of such discriminating mechanisms is the sodium pump, which enables the cells to concentrate potassium and reject sodium (see Hodgkin, 1951). The sodium pump is one of the most fundamental properties of all cells; its operation results in an asymmetric distribution of sodium and potassium between the inner and the outer medium of most cell types. In fact, sodium, which is the prevailing cation in all body fluids (and in the case of the marine organisms, of their outer world in general) is present only in traces in the cytoplasm, in which the prevailing cation is instead potassium. Associated with this unequal distribution of ions is a potential difference across the membrane, the cell interior being negative with respect to the outside: this is the membrane potential, whose value is approximately proportional to the ratio between the concentration of K^+ at the two sides of the membrane: E (in mv) $= -58 \log \dfrac{(K^+) \text{ inside}}{(K^+) \text{ outside}}$. In the sea urchin egg there is presumably an active sodium pump, resulting in a concentration of potassium inside about 17 to 19 times greater than that in the sea water (Rothschild and Barnes, 1953; Tyler et al., 1956). A membrane potential close to the value expected from this difference is present in the unfertilized egg of a number of echinoderms (Tyler et al., 1956; Hiramoto, 1959a), and the dependence of the membrane potential on the external concentration of potassium has also been shown (Tyler et al., 1956). Membrane potentials of the right order of magnitude have also been found in the fish (Ito and Maeno, 1960) and in the amphibian egg (Maeno, 1959).

There are data in the recent literature indicating that at least in the membrane of the crab nerve and of human erythrocytes a membrane-located ATPase is part of the system of sodium and potassium transport (Skou, 1957; Post *et al.*, 1960). A similar situation has been indicated in the cortex of the sea urchin egg (Ohnishi, 1963).

STRUCTURE OF THE EGG SURFACE
AND ITS CHANGES AT FERTILIZATION

In the echinoderm egg

Before analyzing the physiological and biochemical aspects of the surface changes of the egg at fertilization, let us consider more closely the structure of the surface of the mature sea urchin egg and the changes it undergoes upon fertilization. Until the advent of electron microscopy, information regarding the structure of the cell membrane of the egg was mostly indirect. It was mainly based on observations with dark field illumination or polarized light, and on the results of physiological experiments. The ill-defined term "cortex" was used to indicate the whole of the outer layers of the egg which appeared somehow to be involved in the first reaction of the egg to the stimulus of the fertilizing spermatozoon. The study of the surface of the echinoderm egg in polarized light had suggested a number of conclusions about its molecular architecture. From the combination of direct observation of the birefringence of this layer and of its changes under different experimental conditions (Runnström *et al.*, 1943; Monroy and Monroy Oddo, 1946; Monroy, 1947) it was suggested that the "cortex" follows the conventional model of the cell membrane, that is, it is made up of alternate leaflets of lipids and proteins. The lipid molecules were thought to be arranged with their axes perpendicular to the surface of the egg, whereas the proteins were presumed to be oriented with the long axes of the molecules parallel to the surface. This model was later questioned by Mitchison (1952), who suggested instead a mainly protein structure consisting of looped protein molecules arranged in several layers and having the axes of the micelles lying parallel to the surface. A lipid "permeability layer" about 40 A thick would then cover the cortex at its outside.

Evidence of physico-chemical changes taking place in the surface layers of the sea urchin egg as a result of fertilization had been given long ago by Runnström (1928). By means of dark field illumination, he observed that immediately following fertilization, the interference color of the surface changed from yellow-red to silver-white. Runnström suggested that the change might be due to a changed dispersity of the lipids, which he believed to be the major constituents of the egg surface layers. Later on, examination in polarized light (Monroy, 1945; Monroy and Montalenti, 1947; Monroy, 1947) showed that fertilization or chemical activation causes a disappearance of the surface birefringence of the unfertilized egg. This was interpreted as due to a disarrangement of the ordered molecular texture of the lipoprotein layers of the surface. The structural alteration of the egg surface, revealed by the electron microscope, will be described presently. It is so extensive that it well accounts for the optical changes.

Studies with the electron microscope (Afzelius, 1956; Balinsky, 1960; Endo, 1961a; Wolpert and Mercer, 1961; Mercer and Wolpert, 1962) have now shown that the surface of the unfertilized sea urchin egg is bounded by two distinct membranes: the outer one is the vitelline membrane (which following fertilization will become the outer layer of the fertilization membrane); the inner one is the egg plasma membrane. The total thickness of the two membranes together does not exceed 200 A.

Beneath the egg plasma membrane, and in close contact with it, there is an array of "cortical granules" about 0.8 μ in diameter which are also visible with the light microscope. The granules are bounded by a membrane about 50 to 80 A thick, enclosing a dark body which in some species looks like a rolled sheet embedded in a mass of electron-clear material (Fig. 4–1B). Attached to the inner surface of the membrane of the granules are a number of hemispheric globules (Figs. 4–1A, B and 4–2A) with their convex parts bulging towards the inside of the granule (McCulloch, 1952; Afzelius, 1956; Endo, 1961a). Such globules are lacking in the granules of some species.

It was known from studies with the light microscope that upon fertilization the cortical granules are extruded from the egg, at least in part join the vitelline membrane—which meanwhile is being lifted up—and become incorporated into it.

This membrane made up of the vitelline membrane *plus* material of the cortical granules is the fertilization membrane (Moser,

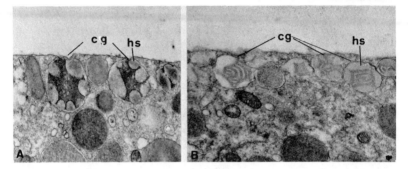

Fig. 4–1. Electron micrographs of the surface of unfertilized eggs of *Arbacia lixula* (A) and *Paracentrotus lividus* (B). The micrographs are intended to show the structure of cortical granules (*cg*) in the two species; dark bodies have a finely granular structure in *Arbacia*, whereas in *Paracentrotus* they look like rolled sheets. Plasma membrane and vitelline membrane are undistinguishable; *hs*, hemispheric globules. (Courtesy of Dr. G. Millonig.)

1939; Motomura, 1941; Runnström *et al.*, 1944; Endo, 1952, 1961b). These studies had also shown that the hardening of the fertilization membrane depended on the incorporation of cortical granule material. The fully formed fertilization membrane exhibits a strong positive birefringence (with respect to the tangential direction) which is evidence of a texture with elongated micelles oriented parallel to the surface.

Studies with the electron microscope have shown (Afzelius, 1956; Endo, 1961a) that the cortical granules are not expelled as such but rather undergo a sort of explosion. This consists in the rupture of the membrane of the granule, accompanied by the rupture of the egg plasma membrane at the point where the two membranes come into contact. There are four results: (1) At the point of rupture *the membrane of the granule becomes continuous with the plasma membrane of the egg* (Fig. 4–2B). (2) At the same time the dark bodies of the granules are ejected and become attached to the inner surface of the vitelline membrane now being lifted up (Figs. 4–2B, C and 4–3A). (3) The hemispheric globules then join, building up a continuous layer covering the new egg surface: this is the hyaline layer (Figs. 4–2B, C and 4–3B). In those eggs in which such globules are not present, the hyaline layer is formed as a result of precipitation at the egg surface of a material

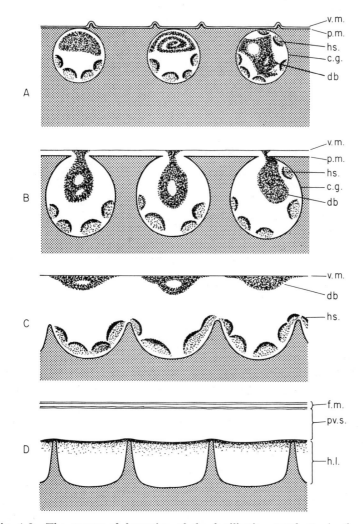

Fig. 4–2. The process of formation of the fertilization membrane in the sea urchin egg. (A) Surface of the unfertilized egg. (B) Explosion of the cortical granules (*cg*): the vitelline membrane (*vm*) begins to be lifted up while the dark bodies (*db*) are extruded and the egg plasma membrane (*pm*) has become continuous with the membrane bounding the cortical granules. (C) The dark bodies have joined the vitelline membrane; the hemispheric globules (*hs*) begin to build up a layer over the new egg surface; this will then become the hyaline layer (*hl*) as indicated in (D). (D) The dark bodies have become fused with the vitelline membrane, thus giving rise to the definitive fertilization membrane (*fm*). *pv.s.*, perivitelline space. (From Endo, 1961a.)

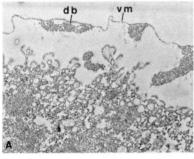

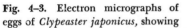

Fig. 4–3. Electron micrographs of eggs of *Clypeaster japonicus,* showing two stages in the formation of the fertilization membrane. (A) Dark bodies (*db*) of the cortical granules attached to the inner surface of the vitelline membrane (*vm*). (corresponds to stage (C) of Fig. 4–2). (B) Fully formed fertilization membrane (*fm*), *hs,* hemispheric bodies in the process of becoming the hyaline layer. (From Endo, 1961.)

also probably deriving from the cortical globules (Afzelius, 1956; Millonig, unpublished); (4) There probably occurs also an extrusion of a liquid from the open cortical granules which fills up the perivitelline space. This liquid contains a sulfated mucopolysaccharide (Immers, 1961), which is consistent with the presence of mucopolysaccharides in the cortical granules (Monné and Hårde, 1951).

A somewhat different model to account for the extrusion of the cortical granules has been suggested by Wolpert and Mercer (1961). According to this, the membrane bounding the granules is merely an inpocketing of the egg plasma membrane. The release of the granules would thus result from the opening of the pockets due to some tension that at the moment of fertilization develops at the surface of the egg. The implications of this view are (a) that the cortical granules lie *at the outside* of the plasma membrane and (b) that the membrane is not ruptured in the process of release of the granules. The question of the relationships of the cortical granules with the plasma membrane will probably be settled by the study of the differentiation of the cortical granules during the maturation of the egg.

From the former interpretation of the process of extrusion of the cortical granules it follows that the surface of the fertilized egg is a mosaic in which patches made up of the original plasma membrane of the unfertilized egg alternate with areas bounded by the former membrane of the cortical granules. On the other hand, the situation as visualized by Wolpert and Mercer does not imply any such structural rearrangement.

In the starfish egg, the vitelline membrane is a thick discrete structure already present in the oocyte; in this membrane broad microvilli are anchored (Fig. 4–4A). The first visible change upon fertilization is a rapid withdrawal of the microvilli followed by the elevation of the vitelline membrane. Then, just as in the sea urchin egg, the cortical granules explode and the dark bodies join the vitelline membrane, which is thus turned into the fertilization membrane (Millonig, unpublished) (Fig. 4–4B).

As already mentioned, starting from the point of sperm attachment, the vitelline membrane detaches itself from the egg plasma membrane while its surface expands considerably (Fig. 3–13); probably it is this expansion which causes the detachment from the plasma membrane. The simplest interpretation to account

Fig. 4–4. Electron micrographs of (A) The surface of an unfertilized egg of *Asterias forbesii*, with thick vitelline membrane (*vm*) on which microvilli (*mv*) are anchored. *cg*, cortical granules. (B) A newly fertilized egg: vitelline membrane with an attached dark body (*db*) of the cortical granules. Other dark bodies still in the perivitelline space; retraction of microvilli. (Courtesy of Dr. G. Millonig.)

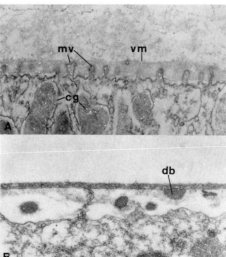

for the expansion of the membrane is the uncoiling of coiled protein molecules (Monroy, 1949).

The process by which the dark bodies of the cortical granules become incorporated into the structure of the fertilization membrane is not known. The electron microscope shows that upon being released, they first acquire a granular structure. The process whereby they fuse with the membrane most probably involves a fibrous or lamellar transformation. This is suggested by the changes the dark bodies undergo in the perivitelline space on some occasions when their fusion with the membrane is prevented. In such cases the light microscope shows that they all suddenly turn into small rods (Runnström, 1948; Endo, 1952). In the electron microscope the rods have a lamellar structure (Endo, 1961a). In the process of hardening of the fertilization membrane an oxidation of −SH groups seems to occur. Indeed, as a result of treatment with thioglycholate, the fertilization membrane loses its toughness, becomes elastic and sensitive to proteolytic enzymes. Probably the reaction underlying the hardening of the membrane is similar to keratinization (Monroy, 1949; Monroy and Runnström, 1948). How the whole process is brought about and controlled is not known. The detachment and expansion of the vitelline membrane and the explosion of the cortical granules are both initiated at the point of entrance of the fertilizing spermatozoon. It seems probable that both processes may be brought about by a single phenomenon. Since these changes occur also in the chemically activated eggs, they are likely to be caused by the triggering of some reaction which then propagates all over the surface of the egg. Finally, all these processes are energy dependent. In fact, breakdown of the cortical granules and elevation of the fertilization membrane are inhibited by uncouplers of oxidative phosphorylation (Okazaki, 1956).

The importance of these observations is that they show that the surface of the fertilized egg is structurally quite different from that of the unfertilized egg. This has to be kept in mind in attempts to interpret the physiology of the cortical changes in relation to fertilization.

In other animals

The presence near the egg surface of granules or vacuoles which as a result of fertilization are either expelled to participate in the formation of a membranous structure, or simply explode and release some substance forming a gelatinous coat around the egg, is a quite widespread occurrence. The inference as to its fundamental importance in the process of activation seems therefore almost unavoidable.

The most spectacular process of vacuole breakdown and secretion of a gelatinous material around the egg is offered by the egg of the polychaete worm, *Nereis,* studied by F. R. Lillie (1911, 1912). The large, clear subcortical vacuoles present in the unfertilized *Nereis* egg break up following fertilization and extrude their contents *through* both the plasma and the vitelline membranes, giving rise to a huge mucous cap all around the egg.

Vacuoles with a polysaccharide content are also present near the surface of the egg of the teleostean fishes (summarized by Rothschild, 1958* and Yamamoto, 1961*). Starting from the point of the sperm entrance at the animal pole (through the micropile), the cortical vacuoles begin to disintegrate (Fig. 4–5), their contents being forced out (Kusa, 1956). At the same time, the egg shrinks and the chorion, which has adhered to the surface of the unfertilized egg, is detached from the egg surface and becomes tougher (Fig. 3–1). The perivitelline space thus appears. Therefore, although in

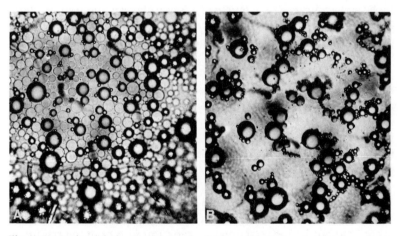

Fig. 4–5. Surface of the egg of *Oryzias latipes*. (A) Before fertilization, showing cortical alveoli and oil drops (the dark spheres). (B) Upon fertilization the cortical alveoli explode. (Courtesy of Dr. E. Nakano.)

this case there is no visual evidence that the material of the vacuoles is incorporated into the chorion, a reaction between the chorion and some component of the vacuoles which results in the hardening of the chorion must be assumed (Nakano, 1956). However, Zotin (1958) has produced data suggesting that the hardening of the membrane may be catalyzed by an enzyme which is not a component of the cortical vacuoles, but is secreted by the egg cytoplasm. The eggs of the acipenserids (Dettlaff, 1962) are particularly interesting as they contain cortical granules, largely made up of acid mucopolysaccharides, which are expelled upon fertilization or artificial activation and become incorporated into the inner membrane. However, in these eggs the formation of the perivitelline space is related to the extrusion of a clear, colloidlike material (apparently not a sulfated acid mucopolysaccharide) present in some globules. These globules, in the unfertilized egg, are deeply embedded in the cytoplasm, and *following activation,* they gradually migrate toward the egg surface. It is the liquid extruding from these vacuoles that gives rise to the perivitelline space and fluid.

Granules largely made up of sulfated acid mucopolysaccharides are also present close to the surface of the mature amphibian egg. Upon fertilization they disappear (Osanai, 1960a), while at the same time the perivitelline space is formed; its contents also proves to be an acidic sulfated mucopolysaccharide. An interesting point is that after the extrusion of the cortical granules, a thin layer appears at the surface of the egg which gives a positive periodic acid-Schiff (PAS) reaction.

Also in the mammalian egg (hamster: Austin, 1956, and rabbit: Hadék, 1963b, c), the presence in the unfertilized egg of cortical granules which disappear following fertilization has been described. Too little is known at present about the cortical granules of the mammalian egg for anything to be said as to their role in fertilization in general, and in the formation and/or widening of the perivitelline space in particular. There is, however, evidence that upon fertilization some change occurs in the zona pellucida which, as will be discussed later, helps to prevent polyspermic fertilization. By analogy with what happens in other eggs, this change might be brought about by the secretion of some substance from the egg upon fertilization. It is indeed well known (see Austin, 1961*, for a review) that soon after fertilization the mammalian egg undergoes a considerable decrease in volume which results in the widening of the perivitelline space.

There are, however, eggs in which cortical granules exist but do not undergo any visible change as a result of fertilization (as in *Spisula:* Rebhun, 1962a, b). However, in *Spisula* (Rebhun, 1962b), following fertilization, the structure of the vitelline membrane exhibits a change which suggests that a reaction with some substance secreted by the egg may have taken place. In the egg of *Barnea*, Pasteels and de Harven (1962) have noted an opening of cortical granules and emptying of their contents towards the inside of the cytoplasm *independently* of fertilization. In fact, they have observed that the explosion of the granules takes place with the same frequency in the unfertilized egg as in the cleavage stages. (See addendum 4–1.)

CHANGES IN PERMEABILITY AND IN THE ELECTRICAL PROPERTIES OF THE EGG MEMBRANE FOLLOWING FERTILIZATION

Almost half a century ago, R. S. Lillie (1916) stressed the similarity between fertilization and stimulation of a nerve or a muscle fiber. The main observation that led him to this suggestion was the increased permeability to water of the sea urchin egg following fertilization. That such a transient or permanent change of "permeability" follows fertilization has been repeatedly confirmed. The quotation marks emphasize the vagueness of the word. In this context it will be used simply to mean that the rate of traffic across the egg membrane is either temporarily or permanently altered as a result of fertilization. Detailed studies (Ishikawa, 1954) have shown that the permeability of the sea urchin egg to water increases rapidly, reaching a maximum about 3 minutes after fertilization, then drops almost to the level of the unfertilized egg, and increases rapidly again about 15 minutes after fertilization. However, the situation is not so clear for the eggs of other animals, and indeed we do not seem to be in a position to form even a tentatively coherent picture. In fact, the fish egg which is readily permeable to water before fertilization, becomes largely impermeable to it, when fertilized (Ito, 1960). In some amphibians (*Rana:*

Picken and Rothschild, 1948) there is also a decreased permeability to water after fertilization, whereas in others (*Hynobius:* Kusa, 1951) no change at all occurs. Evidently more extensive comparative studies are still needed.

In the case of phosphate, Lindberg (1950) had shown that while the unfertilized sea urchin egg is almost impermeable to it, the fertilized egg takes up and metabolizes phosphate very actively. He had further suggested the cortical location of an ATP-synthesizing system the activity of which increases considerably following fertilization.

More recent experiments by Litchfield and Whiteley (1959) and Whiteley and Chambers (1960) have presented convincing evidence of the differentiation of a cortical phosphate transport mechanism within a few minutes after fertilization. The rate of uptake of ^{32}P by the unfertilized eggs is nearly zero and remains such during the first 15 minutes or so after fertilization (lag phase); it then increases rapidly to become maximal 30 to 60 minutes after fertilization (Fig. 4–6). Dinitrophenol, azide, cyanide, and anaerobiosis cause a marked inhibition of the formation of the transport mechanism when they are applied during the lag phase, but they are ineffective if applied after this (Fig. 4–6). This would suggest that these agents interfere with the processes underlying *the formation* of the system but not with the *activity* of the system itself. The surface location of the system is indicated by its equal distribution in egg fragments stratified by centrifugation. It is interesting that in eggs submitted to high hydrostatic pressure within 20 seconds after fertilization in which the breakdown of the cortical granules is blocked, the transport mechanism differentiates (Chase, quoted by Whiteley and Chambers, 1960). The general conclusion of these experiments is that as a result of fertilization a surface-located enzyme mechanism which is responsible for the phosphate transport is synthesized *de novo* in the egg.

As will be discussed in Chapter Six, the rate of amino acid penetration in the echinoderm egg is also greatly increased after fertilization, but nothing is known as to the processes underlying the change. In the frog oocyte, amino acid transport is sodium dependent (Mirsky, personal communication) just as it is across the nuclear membrane (Allfrey *et al.*, 1961). Since sodium content in the unfertilized egg of the echinoderms is exceedingly low (page 47) it would be interesting to find out whether following fertiliza-

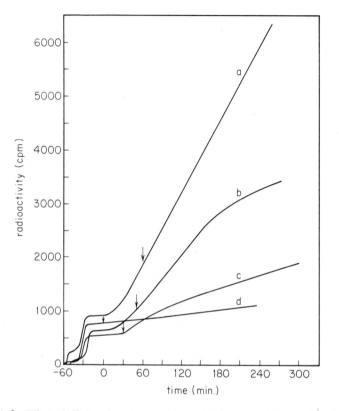

Fig. 4–6. Effect of dinitrophenol on uptake of ^{32}P by eggs of *Strongylocentrotus purpuratus*. At zero time, eggs were inseminated, and then at the point indicated by arrows, $10^{-4}M$ dinitrophenol was added. The experiment shows that addition at the time of fertilization (curve *d*) completely inhibits the increase in rate of uptake, whereas the addition 60 minutes after fertilization (curve *a*) is fully ineffective. (From Litchfield and Whiteley, 1959.)

tion this condition undergoes any change. Actually, there is an observation of Brooks (1939) who described an accumulation of Na⁺ in the egg of *Urechis* following fertilization.

As mentioned before, a study of the permeability changes in the egg at fertilization had led R. S. Lillie to suggest an analogy between the elementary processes of the activation of the egg and those of nerve stimulation. Lillie's suggestion prompted a number of investigations aimed at finding out whether or not changes in the electrical properties of the egg membrane in conjunction with fertilization could be detected. The first attempts were most disappointing, owing to uncertainty that the egg membrane was actually pierced by the microelectrodes. This was shown to be due to the tremendous extensibility of the egg cortex, which passively covers the microelectrodes like a sleeve while they are being pushed against the egg surface (Tyler and Monroy, 1955). Once this difficulty had been overcome, it became possible to study the changes in the electrical properties of the membrane following fertilization. Some reliable measurements are now available for the eggs of the echinoderms, fishes, and amphibians. In the echinoderm egg, membrane potentials as high as 40 to 60 mv (inside negative) have been found in *Asterias forbesii* (Grundfest, Kao, Monroy, and Tyler, 1955; Tyler, Monroy, Kao, and Grundfest, 1956) whereas lower values have been recorded in sea urchin eggs (for example, in *Peronella lesueuri* from 5.2 to 32.3, Hiramoto, 1959a, b). A transient change of a few millivolts lasting about one minute was always recorded in conjunction with fertilization (Fig. 4–7). In *Asterias forbesii*, the membrane potential started to change in conjunction with the beginning of the visible surface changes of the egg and was practically terminated with the elevation of the fertilization membrane (Tyler *et al.*, 1956). In *Peronella* (but not in *Asterias*) at the same time the membrane resistance drops from about 3940 to 2380 ohm/cm^2 (Hiramoto, 1959a, b). This drop in the membrane resistance is consistent with the observed transient increased permeability to water. In the sea urchin egg the membrane capacitance increases considerably after fertilization (Cole, 1938; Cole and Spencer, 1938; Iida, 1949): this is consistent with the increase of the surface area of the egg following fertilization (see page 50). Simultaneously with these phenomena, as was theoretically to be expected, a transient release of K^+ has been detected (Tyler and Monroy, 1959). Although technically difficult, it would certainly be most interesting to find out whether, just as in the stimulation of a nerve, so also in the egg a transient intake of Na^+ occurs in conjunction with fertilization.

Also in the cyprinoid fish, *Oryzias latipes,* it has been shown that when the electrode is successfully inserted into the egg, a membrane potential, inside negative, is recorded in the unfertilized egg (Maeno *et al.*, 1956; Ito and Maeno, 1960; Ito, 1962). When the egg was fertilized, coinciding with the breakdown of the cortical alveoli an increase of the potential was observed (hyperpolarization

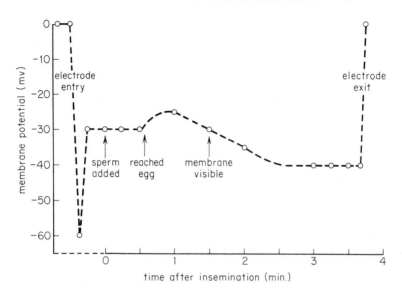

Fig. 4–7. Membrane potential of *Asterias* egg and its changes on fertilization. Upon successful insertion of the electrode a transient potential difference of 60 mv (inside negative) is recorded; then the membrane potential is stabilized at about −30 mv. Within 30 seconds after addition of sperm, the potential decreased by about 5 mv. Subsequently the potential increased again and remained steady at −40 mv. (From Tyler, Monroy, Kao, and Grundfest, 1956.)

of the membrane), together with a slow decrease of the membrane resistance. However, Kao (1955) has failed to detect any membrane potential either before or after fertilization of the *Fundulus* egg; only the membrane resistance increased considerably following activation.

As mentioned earlier in this chapter, in the course of maturation the toad (*Bufo*) egg (Maeno, 1959) becomes progressively impermeable to K+, and the membrane resistance increases to very high values (200 Kohm/cm²). Upon fertilization or mechanical activation, in this case, too, a slow change in the membrane potential occurs, with an occasional overshoot of about 50 mv. In this egg, however, there is a permeability increase only in chloride and in sodium. Much more work is still required before the significance of the electrical properties of the egg membrane and of their changes following fertilization can be understood. Nevertheless, it seems safe to state that fertilization can be considered as a phenomenon of cell stimulation; in this sense the comparison with the events taking place in the nerve may be illuminating. However, the fundamental difference that must be stressed is that in the nerve or muscle the membrane change is *transient,* whereas in the egg it is *permanent,* as it involves extensive structural rearrangements.

THE POLYSPERMY-PREVENTING REACTION

One of the most important physiological expressions of the changes the egg surface undergoes at fertilization is the reaction that makes it unresponsive to additional spermatozoa, after the first one has established successful contact with it.

Just (1919) described this reaction as a "negativity wave" sweeping all over the egg surface, starting from the point of entrance of the fertilizing spermatozoon.

In the analysis of this reaction the two main questions are (1) whether the polyspermy-preventing mechanisms reside in the cell (plasma) membrane of the egg or in its accessory membranes and/or coats; and (2) whether anything can be said as to the basic structural and chemical mechanisms underlying this reaction.

As to question (1), the situation appears somewhat different even among animals belonging to closely related genera. Although more extensive investigations are needed, the impression one receives is that in the course of evolution the mechanisms protecting the egg against polyspermic insemination have been shared between the egg cell (plasma) membrane proper and its accessory membranes (vitelline membrane, chorion, etc.), sometimes being localized in the former and sometimes in the latter.

Among the sea urchins, the mechanical removal of the fertilization membrane makes the eggs of *Lytechinus pictus* and *Lytechinus variegatus* freely accessible to further spermatozoa (Tyler, Monroy, and Metz, 1956) and the same is true for the closely related Mediterranean genus, *Psammechinus* (Monroy, unpublished). The eggs of *Dendraster excentricus* (Tyler, Monroy, and Metz, 1956) and of *Paracentrotus lividus* (Monroy, unpublished) on the contrary, remained unresponsive in spite of demembranation.

Evidently, in the latter case the polyspermy-preventing mechanisms reside *also* in the egg cell membrane.

A noteworthy condition is that of the ascidian egg. The ascidians are hermaphroditic animals in which the maturation of both male and female gametes occurs at the same time but the eggs are not fertilized by the spermatozoa produced by the same individual: this is the so-called self-sterility. Now, it was discovered by Morgan (1923) that in *Ciona* the self-sterility factors reside in the chorion, and indeed its removal allows the egg to be self-fertilized. The removal of the egg membrane also makes fertilization with heterologous spermatozoa possible (Reverberi, 1933; Minganti, 1948, 1950). On the other hand, eggs mechanically denuded of their chorion and test cells do not become polyspermic (Ortolani, personal communication) thus showing that the polyspermy-preventing mechanisms reside in the egg surface.

In mammals, the polyspermy-preventing mechanism seems to be at least partly located on the zona pellucida. Upon penetration of one spermatozoon, the zona undergoes some change that makes it either completely impermeable (highly efficient reaction, as in the hamster and dog) or less permeable (moderately efficient reaction, as in rat and mouse) to additional spermatozoa. This is the so-called *zona reaction* (Braden *et al.*, 1954). There are mammals, however, such as the rabbit, in which the zona reaction seems to be lacking (for a review, see Austin, 1961*). In these eggs, as well as in those in which the efficiency of the zona reaction is moderate, a number of spermatozoa can be seen in the perivitelline space: nevertheless the eggs remain monospermic. This would seem to indicate some additional, and probably pre-eminent, mechanism residing in the egg surface. (See addendum 4–2.)

A further interesting feature is offered by the monospermic fish eggs. In these eggs sperm penetration occurs through a micropylar canal at the animal pole. The observations of K. Yamamoto (quoted in T. Yamamoto, 1961*) and Sakai (1961) have established that once a spermatozoon has reached the egg surface and entered the egg, the supernumerary spermatozoa are pushed out by some "colloid secretion." Most likely, this is the product of the breakdown of the cortical vacuoles, that is, the perivitelline fluid. Next, the micropylar canal is plugged by some material at present of unknown nature. Now the work of Ginsburg (1961) has shown that in the sturgeon the block against polyspermy has the same time course as the discharge of the cortical alveoli; indeed the perivitelline fluid appears to be the effective agent in protecting the egg against polyspermy. If this is washed away, the egg can be made polyspermic. This points to the existence of still another possible mechanism involved in polyspermy prevention.

In contrast to the cases so far described, the eggs of many insects, amphibians, reptiles, and birds are normally entered by many spermatozoa; only one, however, eventually fuses with the egg pronucleus, the supernumerary ones being somehow destroyed (see Rothschild, 1954*, for a review). One of the most interesting examples is offered by the urodele eggs studied in detail by Fankhauser (1925, 1932, 1948). In *Triturus*, up to nine spermatozoa can enter an egg. At first, all sperm nuclei undergo the same changes and give rise to asters, which while enlarging repel each other. However, as soon as one sperm nucleus fuses with the egg nucleus, degeneration of the supernumerary sperm nuclei begins; the closer they are to the zygote nucleus the sooner they degenerate. This suggests the spreading of a factor of some kind from the zygote nucleus as soon as it is formed, which specifically acts on the supernumerary nuclei. This suggestion is supported by experiments (Fankhauser, 1925) in which eggs were constricted with a fine thread soon after fertilization. If the bridge connecting the two halves was thin, the supernumerary sperm nuclei in the half lacking the zygote nucleus were able to go on dividing. On the contrary, if the connecting bridge was wider than one half the diameter of the egg, they degenerated just as in an unconstricted egg. These observations are certainly of great interest; the influence exerted by the zygote nucleus on the supernumerary sperm nuclei may indeed be the first, or at least one of the earliest expressions of the activity of the zygote nucleus.

A brief digression into the plant kingdom seems here quite to the point. In some plants, such as the Cruciferae, the mechanisms preventing self-fertilization reside in the stigmatic surface of the pistil. This surface gives rise to a number of papillae made up of cellulose and coated by a cuticle and pectin. The pollen grains attach to the papillae and it has been shown that they are endowed with an enzyme, cutinase, which is able to break down the cuticle, thus allowing the pollen tube to grow within the pistil. In the case of self-pollination, however, the enzymatic system is either inactivated or its activation is somehow inhibited. In fact the barrier can be overcome either by an enzymatic predigestion of the cuticle or by implanting the pollen grains directly into the body of the stigma (see Kroh and Linskens, 1963a, b). Even more interesting is the observation that pollens which have been kept for some time on a foreign stigma become able to penetrate the self-stigma (Kroh, quoted by Linskens, 1964). Another type of incompatibility in self-fertilization is observed in the Solanaceae, in which the pollen tube can form, and in fact enters the style, but is soon or later arrested in its growth. In this case a great deposit of cellulose fibrils and callose plugs occurs all around the growing tip of the tube (Mühle-thaler and Linskens, 1956). It has been shown that this is due to an altered carbohydrate metabolism (Linskens, 1955). The electrophoretic analysis of extracts of pistils after compatible and incompatible combinations has shown that in the latter, as a result of pollination, two protein components can be identified, whereas in the compatible combination only one appears (Linskens, 1953, 1955). To the knowledge of the present writer, this is the first instance in which the appearance of *specific* proteins has been shown as an immediate result of fertilization. Furthermore, incompatibility has been explained on a genetic-immunological basis (East, 1929). It has been suggested that when a pollen tube carrying the incompatibility allele S_1 enters a pistil having an S_1S_1 or S_1S_x constitution, it acts as an antigen and causes the formation of antibodies against the S_1 tube. This situation opens up new and exciting possibilities in the study of gene-controlled protein synthesis and the problem of differentiation (see Linskens, 1964).

Very little is known about the molecular basis of the changes in the egg cell membrane underlying the polyspermy-preventing reaction. Tyler (1959, 1960) has drawn attention to the possible role of the microvilli protruding from the egg surface. Recent electron microscope work has shown that the surface of a number of eggs extends in the form of microvilli through the vitelline membrane and/or egg coats (Sotelo and Porter in the rat, 1959; Rebhun in *Spisula*, 1962; Pasteels and de Harven in *Barnea*, 1962; Humphreys, 1962, J. Dan, 1962, in *Mytilus*; Millonig in the starfish, unpublished). The tips of the microvilli are always covered by a thin layer of the vitelline membrane. According to Tyler, the rapid retraction of the microvilli following the attachment of the successful spermatozoon to one of them should provide the morphological basis for the polyspermy-preventing reaction. However, in none of the above-mentioned eggs has any change in the microvilli been noticed following fertilization. Only in *Asterias* (Millonig, unpublished) is the elevation of the fertilization membrane accompanied by a withdrawal of the microvilli, which in the unfertilized eggs penetrate the thick vitelline membrane. A similar situation may also be present in the egg of *Sabellaria* (Novikoff, 1939), which, however, has not yet been studied with the electron microscope. The surface of the mature egg appears to be connected to the vitelline membrane by means of a number of tiny filaments which rapidly withdraw while the fertilizing spermatozoon passes into the egg interior. Even if such a retraction occurs in some eggs, it cannot be considered a general phenomenon. It seems more likely that the polyspermy-preventing reaction rests on much more subtle structural changes at the molecular level of the surface of the egg. (See addendum 4–3.)

In the sea urchin egg, the elegant work of Rothschild and Swann (1949, 1950, 1951a, b, 1952) has shown that fertilization brings about in the egg surface (1) a rapid change (taking about 2 seconds) which although not affording complete protection against the penetration of further spermatozoa, does decrease its reactivity; (2) a slow change which in about one minute establishes a complete refractoriness of the egg surface. The time course of propagation of the rapid change roughly coincides with that of the disappearance of the surface birefringence and of the color change observed with dark field illumination. The slow change, on the other hand, coincides with the breakdown of the cortical granules, membrane elevation, transient change in the membrane potential (Tyler, Monroy, Kao, and Grundfest, 1956; Hiramoto, 1959b) and increase in the rate of K^+ exchange (Tyler and Monroy, 1959). The existence of a rapid block has been questioned by Ginsburg (1963), who has given evidence that the only block is actually the slow one, (propagating time 60 to 100 seconds, in *Strongylocentrotus dröbachiensis*) which coincides with the time of propagation of breakdown of the cortical granules.

Hence, one is tempted to suggest a connection between the morphological and the physiological changes, and in particular that the molecular rearrangement of the surface layer of the egg following fertilization brings about its loss of ability to react with spermatozoa.

This view is strengthened by observations that uncouplers of oxidative phosphorylation (Okazaki, 1956) and high hydrostatic pressure (Whiteley and Chambers, 1960) inhibit both the breakdown of the cortical granules and the membrane elevation, *and* the polyspermy-preventing reaction. Also the observation that sea urchin eggs (Hagström and Hagström, 1954; Tyler and Metz, 1955; Tyler, Monroy, and Metz, 1956) and ascidian eggs (Ortolani, personal communication) treated with trypsin show a high incidence of polyspermy, points in the same direction. In the case of the sea urchin egg, the interpretation of this experiment may be ambiguous. In the trypsin-treated eggs the fertilization membrane fails to elevate, most probably due to damage of the vitelline membrane. Hence one might suggest that the damage of this membrane, rather than of the cell (plasma) membrane, is responsible for the loss of the polyspermy-preventing mechanism. However, this interpretation does not apply to the ascidian egg. But even in the case of the sea urchin egg there are experiments which point to the structural alteration of the cell membrane as the cause of its refractoriness in reacting with other spermatozoa. Chemically activated eggs (Ishida and Nakano, 1947, 1950) or fertilized eggs (Sugiyama, 1951) lose their refractoriness to spermatozoa when treated with Ca- and Mg-free sea water. This indicates a rearrangement of the molecular structure of the cell membrane, as a result of activation, in which divalent ions are of importance for the establishment of the condition of refractoriness. It further indicates that the specific reacting groups are not destroyed upon fertilization but only masked or made unreactive as a result of the new molecular arrangement.

A final point to be discussed is why the fertilized sea urchin eggs when reinseminated become polyspermic; in other words, they seem to have lost the ability to develop a propagated response. This may again depend on the difference in molecular texture of the egg cell membrane between unfertilized and fertilized eggs. As discussed earlier, the cell membrane of the latter is a mosaic of areas deriving from the original cell membrane of the unfertilized egg and areas deriving from the membrane of the cortical granules. According to our interpretation, the former still bear (available or masked) the reacting groups with which the spermatozoa can react; the propagation of the reaction of polyspermy prevention is, however, hampered by the areas deriving from the membrane of the cortical granules.

It may be recalled here that sea urchin oocytes can be penetrated by a great number of spermatozoa. When studied in polarized light, they are shown to lack the cortical birefringence which is typical of the mature egg and is an indication of a definite molecular arrangement (Monroy, 1948a). This again emphasizes the fundamental importance of the specific molecular organization of the egg cell membrane for the development of the polyspermy-preventing reaction.

ADDENDUM

4–1. In the echiuroid worms, *Urechis* and *Ikedosoma*, no cortical granules have been found. Therefore the formation of the perivitelline space and fluid must be accounted for as due to a secretion from the egg cytoplasm (Sawada and Noda, 1963 a, b).

SAWADA, N., and NODA, Y., 1963a. "An electron microscope study on the Urechis egg," *Mem. Ehime Univ.* Sect. 2, Ser. B, 4: 539–549.
SAWADA, N., and NODA, Y., 1963b. "Studies on the fertilization in eggs of echiuroid, *Ikedosoma gogoshimense* (Ikeda). 2. Electron microscope studies on the egg," *Mem. Ehime Univ.* Sect. 2, Ser. B, 4: 551–561.

4–2. In the pig egg in which the *zona pellucida* appears to consist of three concentric layers, supernumerary spermatozoa have never been seen deeper than the middle layer (Dickman and Dziuk, 1964).

4–3. In the eggs of the echiuroid worms, *Urechis* and *Ikedosoma*, the microvilli are considerably more prominent in the immature oocytes in the coelomic fluid than in the mature ones in the segmental organs. In the former, in fact, the microvilli protrude at the outside of the vitelline membrane whereas in the latter the outer filaments have disappeared and only the part embedded in the membrane remains. Upon fertilization, as a result of the detachment of the vitelline membrane from the egg surface (which results in the formation of the fertilization membrane and of the peritelline space), the microvilli remain attached to the membrane and hence their connection with the egg surface is broken (Sawada and Noda, 1963 a, b). This writer wonders, however, how sure one can be that such a breakage is not a technical artifact. In any case, the surface of the egg immediately after fertilization becomes smooth; about 30 minutes later new long protoplasmic processes appear that extend in the perivitelline space.

chapter five

Surface Changes, Activation of the Egg, and Formation of the Zygote Nucleus

THE ROLE OF SURFACE CHANGES
IN THE ACTIVATION OF THE EGG

The question of the role of the surface changes in the process of activation may now be discussed. The first point is whether the establishment of contact between the spermatozoon and the egg plasma membrane is sufficient to spark the activation reaction.

This problem was first approached by F. R. Lillie (1912) on the egg of *Nereis*. In *Nereis*, attachment of the spermatozoon to the egg membrane is immediately followed by surface changes and formation of the fertilization cone; however, actual penetration of the spermatozoon does not take place until about 40 minutes later. By analogy with the events in other eggs, most probably the spermatozoon establishes immediate contact with the egg plasma membrane by means of its acrosomal filament, and this is enough to elicit the fertilization reaction. Therefore this would be clear evidence that surface changes may be brought about simply by the interaction with the acrosomal filament, and the suggestion seems reasonable that some substance is hereby "injected" which elicits the reaction. Lillie performed some ingenious experiments by which he succeeded in removing the spermatozoon during its penetration by submitting the egg to centrifugation. By doing so, he observed that in spite of having formed a fertilization membrane, having shown the surface changes, and having undergone maturation, these eggs nevertheless failed to segment. "The partially fertilized eggs, therefore, resemble

69

the normal ones in the fact that membrane formation and the first stimulus to development are called forth by action of the spermatozoon, and they differ from the normally fertilized eggs in that the internal egg protoplasm has not received the direct stimulus of the spermatozoon." These results were later confirmed by Goodrich (1920), who succeeded in removing the spermatozoon by a micrurgical method. A series of detailed experiments on sea urchin eggs have recently been undertaken by Hiramoto (1962b), who has also used the micrurgical method to remove the spermatozoon at various times during fertilization. Hiramoto has found that removal of the spermatozoon either during its attachment or even after it has entered the egg cytoplasm is invariably followed by a parthenogenetic type of activation; that is, the egg undergoes a number of monaster cycles but never cleaves. On the other hand, the removal of the egg nucleus either before or after fertilization is followed by almost normal cleavage. These observations, taken together with those of Lillie and Goodrich, indicate that for the activation proper to occur, the interaction of the spermatozoon with the egg surface is sufficient. In fact, this conclusion may be carried a step further by suggesting, following Hiramoto, that activation is accomplished when the acrosome establishes its contact with the egg.

However, the presence of the spermatozoon is necessary for the establishment of the dicentry of the egg, and hence for cleavage to take place. This conclusion had already been reached by Boveri (1888, 1895), who had suggested that the key event of fertilization was the introduction of the sperm centrosome, which would thus substitute for the egg centrosome that had been lost at some time during maturation.

This idea was stressed by Wilson (1895*) when he wrote:

> Fertilization, accordingly, consists . . . of two distinct phenomena: first, the introduction into the egg of the paternal hereditary characteristics potentially contained in some unknown manner in the substance of the sperm-nucleus or of the chromosomes into which it resolves itself. Second, the introduction into the egg of a centrosome which gives rise to the mechanisms by means of which the egg divides and the hereditary substance is distributed to the resulting cells.

That the sperm-derived centriole acts as an organizer of the asters and of the mitotic spindle of the fertilized egg is quite generally accepted.

However, as Wilson himself showed (1901), asters can form within enucleate parthenogenetically activated eggs, a fact subsequently beautifully demonstrated by the experiments of E. B. Harvey (1936) on the enucleate egg fragments torn apart by centrifugation. Observations with the electron microscope have shown that these asters do contain real centrioles (Dirksen, 1961). This raises a number of questions, notably as to the origin of the centrioles (are they really self-duplicating units? Tyler, 1941*; Brachet, 1957*) and as to the factors which cause their disappearance during maturation and prevent their reappearance in normal fertilization.

The problem now arises, to what extent are the surface changes necessary for the activation of the egg? Motomura (1954) and Osanai (1960b) have conducted experiments on the inhibition of the breakdown of the cortical granules (Motomura by a treatment with permanganate; Osanai with acetone, butyric acid, or lactic acid). The experiments show that the inhibition, although preventing the formation of a normal fertilization membrane and the hyaline layer, does not prevent nuclear and cytoplasmic activation. In the extreme cases of inhibition reported by Osanai, cytoplasmic cleavage was inhibited while nuclear division took place. This would indicate a certain independence of the cytoplasmic and nuclear activation from the surface changes. On the other hand, Allen and Hagström (1955), working on the eggs of sea urchins of the Mediterranean and of the North Sea, obtained results at variance with those of the Japanese workers. In Allen and Hagström's experiments the progress of the surface changes was interrupted by a 20-second exposure to warm sea water containing a small amount of lauryl sulfate. (The interruption was indicated by the failure of the cortical granules to explode and the lack of fertilization membrane over a certain area of the egg surface.) In this case the cytoplasm did not undergo the changes typical of the activated egg. Migration of the pronuclei, expansion of the asters, activation of the nuclei, and nuclear fusion appeared seriously impaired, and sometimes the cleavage furrows were incomplete. However, it seems difficult in these experiments to be sure that the effect of the heat shock and detergent is limited to the surface only, rather than affecting the whole cell.

In the experiments of the Japanese workers, on the other hand, only the surface changes appeared to be inhibited, without cytoplasmic damage, as indicated by the normality of the processes of nuclear and cytoplasmic activation.

Although such an important question certainly deserves much closer examination, the available evidence seems to suggest that the activating reaction may indeed take place in the surface layers, but cytoplasmic and nuclear activation are to a certain extent independent *of the visible* surface change, particularly of the breakdown of the cortical granules. It may rather be surmised that the interaction with the spermatozoon originates a reaction (or, rather, a chain of reactions) in the surface layers of the egg which is responsible both for the breakdown of the cortical granules *and* the activation of the nuclear-cytoplasmic system.

This view is supported by the experiments carried out by T. Yamamoto (1944) on the fish and by Sugiyama (1953a and b; 1956) on the sea urchin egg. The experiments of Yamamoto consisted in displacing by centrifugation the cortical alveoli of the unfertilized *Oryzias* egg. In these eggs, in fact, the cortical alveoli can easily be displaced by centrifugation and accumulate at the centrifugal pole. (In the sea urchin egg, the cortical granules are firmly anchored to the surface.) Now, in spite of the fact that the surface is deprived of the alveoli, these eggs can be activated both by normal fertilization and by pricking. It is also important to note that in such eggs, the alveoli which happen to be embedded in the yolk fail to break up. These results have led T. Yamamoto (1944) to make the suggestion that fertilization or artificial activation gives rise to some sort of propagating change, called the "fertilization wave," which causes both the activation of the egg *and* the breakdown of the cortical alveoli. This latter therefore is not involved in the primary events of fertilization.

In the sea urchin egg, Sugiyama (summarized in 1956) has shown that some activating agents such as wasp venom and sodium choleinate, when acting on a small area of the egg surface, bring about a breakdown of the cortical granules accompanied by membrane elevation confined to the area acted upon by the reagent. Hence the breakdown of a cortical granule *cannot* cause its neighboring granules to explode: in other words, the chainlike explosion of the cortical granules occurring at fertilization is not caused by some substance diffusing from one exploding granule to the next. That is, the process is not self-propagating. On the other hand, when a limited area of the egg surface is exposed to such reagents as butyric acid or urea, granule breakdown rapidly propagates to the whole unexposed surface of the egg. Sugiyama concludes that in such a case a fertilization wave is produced by the reagent, which by virtue of its propagation over the whole egg surface *also* causes the explosion of the cortical granules. It is interesting that eggs "narcotized" with urethane lose the ability to respond either to insemination or to artificial activation. In the case of inseminated eggs, the spermatozoon can enter the egg, but no granule breakdown takes place. However, when such narcotized eggs are exposed to sodium choleinate or wasp venom, explosion of the cortical granules in the contact area takes place. This experiment strengthens the idea that the fertilization wave is a subtle change which can only arise and propagate under normal conditions of excitability of the egg surface. The mathematical analysis of the propagation of the surface changes in the sea urchin egg suggests an autocatalytic process (Kacser, 1955).

The two theories which have exerted the strongest influence on the development of the work on fertilization are J. Loeb's theory of the surface cytolysis and the previously mentioned fertilizin theory of F. R. Lillie (summarized in 1919*). J. Loeb (1913*) suggested that the key event of the activation is a transient surface cytolysis of the egg. According to this theory, the fertilizing spermatozoon, when reacting with the surface of the egg, injects, so to speak, a lysin which enhances a surface cytolysis, as a result of which the activating factor is released. A modification of Loeb's theory was presented by Runnström (1949*). According to this author, an enzyme present in the spermatozoon is responsible for the breakdown of an inhibitor-enzyme complex in the egg surface, thus releasing the enzyme. The reaction is assumed to be self-propagating over the egg surface, and the inhibitor is suggested to be a polysaccharide identical or at least similar to the jelly coat material.

In the theory of F. R. Lillie (1914), already discussed in Chapter Two, activation consists in the reaction of the spermophile (outer) group of one of the (bipolar) fertilizin molecules at the surface of the egg with a sperm receptor (see Fig. 2–2). This reaction starts a chainlike self-propagating response whereby all the fertilizin molecules become activated. The spermophile end of each molecule immediately reacts with an antifertilizin molecule, whereas the ovophile (inner) group reacts with an egg-receptor molecule.

Little or nothing is known of the chemical reactions that occur at the surface of the egg upon fertilization.

The problem is therefore that of defining a propagating chemical change which may in its turn set in motion the fundamental chain of reactions of the activation of the egg. On the basis of some experimental evidence, a modified form of J. Loeb's theory has been presented by Monroy (1956). In this case it is suggested that egg lipases, activated by sperm lipases, bring about a splitting of the phospholipids at the egg surface, with the transient production of lysophosphatides or lysophosphatidelike substances. The hypothesis rested on experiments on a model system which showed that live sea urchin spermatozoa, when acting upon a suspension of lipovitelline, caused a release of phospholipids, which were then rapidly degraded, giving rise to water-soluble hemolytic products (Monroy, 1953, 1956; Maggio and Monroy, 1955). It was thus suggested that the transient release of lysophosphatides may somehow be involved in the activation reaction. That lysophosphatides are effective activators is known (Öhman, 1944).

Admittedly, the extrapolation from model experiments to *in vivo* conditions is not always justified. However, lysolecithin has been identified in the eggs immediately after fertilization, whereas none is present in the unfertilized egg. Furthermore, choline has been found to increase (Numanoi, 1959a). The same author has further shown that the addition of live spermatozoa to a homogenate of unfertilized sea urchin egg results in the formation of lysolecithin (Numanoi, 1959b). Of course, it is difficult to say at present whether or not all these reactions have anything to do with the process of activation: they may indeed be involved in some metabolic process other than activation, or may even be mere artifacts. At any rate they may open the way to new experiments.

THE FUSION OF THE PRONUCLEI

A notable feature of the behavior of the sperm nucleus once inside the egg is the approximately 180° rotation it undergoes, so that now the centrosome comes to be at its front, that is, pointing toward the interior of the egg (Flemming, 1881). One has the impression that the centrosome is leading the way for the advancing sperm nucleus toward the egg nucleus. In some eggs the centrosome may even become separated from the sperm nucleus and move faster than it does (Boveri, 1888).

In eggs that have completed their maturation before fertilization (such as the sea urchin egg), the movement of the sperm nucleus towards the egg interior begins immediately. Soon afterwards also the egg nucleus begins to move, and eventually the two pronuclei meet at or near the center of the egg. On the other hand, if the egg has not initiated or completed its maturation, the sperm remains immotile underneath the egg surface or moves only slightly until after maturation has been completed. Only then does the sperm centrosome become evident and the sperm aster begin to form (see, for example, Conklin, 1901, *Crepidula*).

It has been known for a long time that the path of the sperm nucleus to meet the egg nucleus is often not a straight one but rather curved. We know very little of the causal relationships of the movements of the sperm and egg nucleus before they meet. Indeed, this is a subject that has lately been entirely neglected by the students of fertilization. It seems well worth recalling that quite long ago Giardina (1902a, b) attempted to present a reasonable interpretation of these facts (however naïve it may appear today). He suggested that the sperm centrosome might be the center of diffusion of specific substances which cause the sperm nucleus to move, and that the asymmetry of the shape of the head of the spermatozoon might be the cause of its rotation.

According to the observations of E. L. Chambers (1939), in the sea urchin egg the sperm nucleus is mechanically pushed towards the center of the egg by the growing fibers of the sperm aster. As to the egg nucleus, this begins to move towards the sperm nucleus well before the radiations of the sperm asters have reached it (E. L. Chambers, 1939). The first sign of the activation of the nucleus is its swelling. Now it has been observed that in partially activated eggs drawn in glass capillaries (Allen, 1954; Allen and Hagström, 1955), if the egg nucleus happens to be surrounded by a large area of nonactivated cytoplasm, it fails to move but nevertheless undergoes swelling. This suggests that the factors responsible for the activation of the nucleus can reach it and be effective even through nonactivated cytoplasm. The activated cytoplasm, on the other hand, seems to be a necessary prerequisite for the egg nucleus to move. The fact that the egg nucleus undergoes swelling and migrates to the center of the egg in parthenogenetically activated eggs speaks against the sperm nucleus or the sperm aster as being the center of diffusion of such "substances."

Rather, the changes occurring in the cytoplasm of the egg itself upon activation may bring about these movements. The amoeboid deformations of the egg nucleus while moving (Selenka, 1878; Wilson and Mathews, 1895; Giardina, 1902a, b; E. L. Chambers, 1939) may indicate active and very rapid exchanges taking place across the nuclear membrane.

chapter six

The Metabolic Study
of Fertilization

"The crux of the problem of fertilization lies in the nature of the inhibition of the unfertilized egg."

D. M. Whitaker, 1933

THE PHYSIOLOGY
OF THE MATURATION OF THE EGG

The nuclear maturation of the egg within the ovary progresses to a different stage in different animal species. Indeed, some eggs are shed with the germinal vesicle still intact (as in the starfish, in some mollusks and in polychaetes); in others nuclear maturation begins in the gonad but is arrested at the first maturation division (as in *Ciona* and *Phallusia*) or at the second (as in *Rana*, *Bufo*, and *Oryzias*). In some of these eggs, maturation may then continue and even reach completion after shedding, and independent of fertilization; in others instead the initiation or resumption of the maturation process is triggered by fertilization.

However, *irrespective of the stage of nuclear maturation reached at the time of shedding* (that is, when the eggs are presented for fertilization), *all eggs are fundamentally in the same physiological condition.* In particular, (a) their surface is endowed with all the properties on which the interaction with the spermatozoon depends; (b) they are all in a state of metabolic inhibition.

On the other hand, the reaction of the cytoplasm to the spermatozoon is quite different in the eggs which at the moment of fertilization had already completed nuclear maturation and in those which had not.

77

In the former as soon as it has entered the egg the spermatozoon begins to undergo the changes and the movements leading to the formation of the zygote nucleus. In the latter, on the contrary, the spermatozoon remains immotile and unchanged underneath the egg surface and it is only after the completion of nuclear maturation that the sperm nucleus begins to swell and the sperm aster appears. Evidently, for the sperm nucleus to react, the cytoplasm must have undergone some changes which are apparently controlled by nuclear maturation and may be spoken of as cytoplasmic maturation.

The dependence of cytoplasmic maturation on nuclear maturation was shown several decades ago by the elegant experiments of Delage (1901), who cut the oocytes of *Asterias* into two fragments and tested the response of both of them to fertilization.

If the operation was performed when the germinal vesicle was still intact, only the nucleated fragment cleaved; whereas if it was carried out after the disappearance of the nuclear membrane, even if the nucleolus was still visible, cleavage occurred in both fragments. The experiments further indicated that the percentage of successful fertilization of the nonnucleated fragment decreased after the formation of the first polar body and was practically nil after the formation of the second polar body (Table 3).

Table 3

Result of Fertilization of Nucleated and Nonnucleated Fragments of Oocytes of *Asterias glacialis*

Stage at which the operation was performed	Number of eggs operated on	Response of the nonnucleated fragment	
		Fertilized[a]	Not fertilized
1. Nuclear membrane intact	18	0	18
2. Nuclear membrane wrinkled	14	3 + 5 asters; no cleavage	6
3. Nuclear membrane dissolved	21	17	4
4. After first polar body	7	3	4
5. After second polar body	10	0	10

[a] As judged from whether or not cleavage followed.
Source: Data of Delage, 1901.

These experiments were repeated and confirmed soon after by E. B. Wilson (1903) and Yatzu (1905) in *Cerebratulus*. The latter author was able to show that treatment with calcium chloride brings about the formation of cytasters in the cytoplasm of non-nucleated fragments only if these have been obtained *after* the breakdown of the germinal vesicle. Substantially similar results were obtained by Costello (1940) on the egg of the polychaete worm, *Nereis*, in which only the fragment containing the germinal vesicle could be activated parthenogenetically.

These data show that the breakdown of the germinal vesicle is responsible for activating some process in the cytoplasm of the egg which Delage described as *cytoplasmic maturation*. We have no idea as to the nature of the processes involved in cytoplasmic maturation, but the observations referred to above suggest that the mixing of the material of the nucleoplasm and of the nucleoli with the cytoplasm may be the factor involved.

This brings us to consider one of the most remarkable peculiarities of all eggs, namely that they have a large quantity of DNA in their cytoplasm.

The significance of the cytoplasmic DNA reserve (Hoff-Jørgensen and Zeuthen, 1952; Hoff-Jørgensen, 1954; see also Brachet, 1960*, for a review) is quite puzzling. Recent studies by Brachet and Quertier (1963) have given for the first time the histochemical demonstration of the presence of DNA in the cytoplasm of frog's oocyte and at the same time have provided strong support to the idea that it must have relatively low molecular weight. There is recent evidence that submitting DNA of bacteriophage T4 to shear degradation or to DNAase degradation down to molecular weight of 2.2×10^6 and 5×10^5 respectively does not alter its transforming activity (Veldhuisen *et al.*, 1962). Furthermore it has been shown that polyuridylic acid chains containing as little as three nucleotide triplets are still able to induce *in vitro* polymerization of phenylalanine (Marcus *et al.*, 1963). This shows that cytoplasmic DNA may have a far more important role than that of simply acting as a precursor for DNA synthesis during early development. It may indeed be the source of genetic messages at a time when nuclei are almost exclusively engaged in duplication.

The study of the biochemical events accompanying maturation is made difficult by the fact that they happen within the ovary.

However, by collecting the oocytes directly from the gonad some interesting data have been obtained. Lindahl and Holter (1941) succeeded in measuring the respiration of sea urchin oocytes throughout the process of maturation. They were thus able to establish that as soon as maturation began (as indicated by the breakdown of the germinal vesicle) the rate of oxygen consumption underwent a marked drop, thus reaching the level usually observed in the mature unfertilized egg (Fig. 6–1). In the starfish oocyte, on the other hand, Borei (1948) and Borei and Lybing (1949) observed an increase of respiration beginning at the onset of maturation and reaching a peak at the time of the first maturation division. Then respiration started to decline. (See addendum 6–1.) In the oocytes of the teleostean fish *Oryzias latipes*, an increase of several times in the rate of oxygen consumption takes place during the growth period and is then followed by a sharp drop, coincident with the breakdown of the germinal vesicle (Nakano, 1953) (Fig. 6–2). The lowest level was reached at the time the egg had become fertilizable, which is indicated by the appearance of the cortical alveoli. Though few in number, these observations indicate that either at the onset or in the course of maturation, the respiratory metabolism of the egg undergoes a depression.

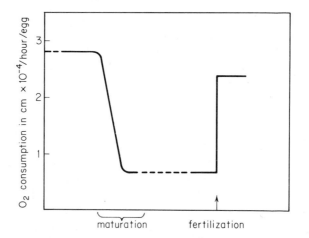

Fig. 6–1. Changes in rate of oxygen consumption during maturation and at the time of fertilization in the egg of *Paracentrotus lividus*. (From Lindahl and Holter, 1941.)

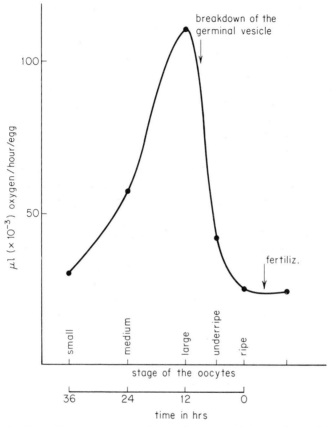

Fig. 6–2. Rate of oxygen consumption in the course of maturation and following fertilization in the egg of *Oryzias latipes*. (Calculated from data of Nakano, 1956.)

Also the incorporation of nucleic acid precursors and of amino acids in the cytoplasm, in the nucleus, and in the nucleolus declines during growth of the starfish oocyte (Ficq, 1955, 1961). When the oocyte is shed, and indeed is ready for fertilization, the ability to incorporate amino acids into proteins is negligible. The same is true for the *Spisula* egg that is fertilized at the primary oocyte stage (Monroy and Tolis, 1964). On the contrary, the sea urchin oocyte is very active in incorporating amino acids into its proteins and this ability is only lost during maturation. A similar situation occurs in the *Oryzias* oocyte in which the incorporating ability suffers a dramatic fall at the onset of maturation (Nakano, personal communication). (See addendum 6–2.)

Thus we reach the important conclusion that the metabolic condition of the eggs at the moment when they are ready for fertilization is independent of the stage of maturation of the nucleus. In other words, whether the fertilizability condition is attained when the germinal vesicle is still intact, or when nuclear maturation has been completed, the egg which is fertilizable, namely physiologically ripe, is in a condition of depressed metabolism. A corollary to this is that the primary oocyte of, for example, *Spisula*, which is indeed physiologically ripe, is analogous (physiologically comparable) to the mature sea urchin egg and *not* to the primary oocyte which is still physiologically unripe.

One might go a step further by suggesting that the metabolic inhibition that builds up in the course of maturation is responsible for the arrest of nuclear maturation. And indeed that the stage to which the nuclear maturation proceeds in the ovary depends on the moment at which the inhibitor reaches the inhibiting threshold value. Fertilization, by removing the block, would then allow nuclear maturation to begin or to proceed to completion.

THE BIOCHEMICAL EVENTS
OF FERTILIZATION

In view of the difficulties of directly approaching the problem of the chemical events of maturation which lead to the establishment of the metabolic block of the ripe egg, the most profitable path is the study of the chemical changes that take place in the egg upon fertilization.

The respiratory metabolism

A milestone in these studies was the observation of Warburg (1910, 1911*) that within a few minutes after fertilization the rate of oxygen consumption of the sea urchin egg increases several fold. This observation seemed to provide the direct proof that the mature unfertilized egg is an inhibited cell and that fertilization releases the inhibition. However, some years later Borei (1948) reported that the respiration of the sea urchin egg declines rapidly after the egg leaves the ovary, and the change that takes place at fertilization only brings the respiratory level back to the level the mature egg originally had in the gonad. Technical difficulties (now overcome) prevented measurements shortly after shedding. Nevertheless, by extrapolating his data to the zero time, Borei concluded that if one could measure the respiration of eggs fertilized very soon after being shed (as may be expected to occur in nature) no respiratory change should be observed. In other words, the low level of respiration of the unfertilized egg does not depend on a decline that takes place during maturation, but rather on the artificial condition of standing in sea water before fertilization. However, recent work by Yasumasu and Nakano (1963) on the eggs of several Japanese sea urchin species have confirmed the original observations of Warburg. In fact these authors have been able to start their observations within a few minutes after the shedding of the eggs, and have thus shown (Fig. 6–3) that (1) the respiration of the unfertilized egg remains constant for several hours, and (2) no matter at what moment after shedding fertilization is accomplished, a sudden rise in the rate of oxygen consumption takes place. These observations have been confirmed by Ohnishi and Sugiyama (1963) who have used the polarographic method of determination of oxygen concentration in the medium in which the eggs were being fertilized. The reason

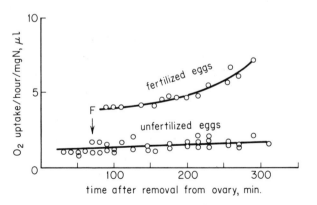

Fig. 6–3. Oxygen uptake of unfertilized and fertilized eggs of *Hemicentrotus pulcherrimus*. *F*, addition of spermatozoa. (From Yasumasu and Nakano, 1963.)

for the peculiar behavior of the eggs studied by Borei is obscure but certainly worth investigating. It must be remembered that along the west coast of Sweden the sea urchins live under extreme conditions of salinity, some being adapted to the high salinity of the depth and others to the almost brackish water near the surface. Whether and how such conditions may influence the physiology of the eggs is unknown but no doubt worth exploring.

When the respiratory change at fertilization was studied carefully and certain precautions were taken to ensure rapid absorption of any released CO_2, it was found that during the first 5 minutes after fertilization the rate of oxygen consumption jumps suddenly to high values, to return just as rapidly almost to the prefertilization level (Laser and Rothschild, 1939) (Fig. 6–4). Soon afterwards the well-known exponential increase of respiration sets in. The first transient jump, as mentioned before, can only be detected if special precautions are taken. In fact, simultaneously with the increase in the rate of oxygen consumption, there is a parallel outburst in the release of CO_2, which, if not rapidly absorbed, will compensate, and even overcompensate, for the manometric depression due to the oxygen consumption. This is why, under the usual experimental conditions, not only is this first phase missed but one even gets the impression that respiration has ceased altogether. This observation has recently been confirmed by the use of a polarographic method to measure oxygen concentration (Ohnishi and Sugiyama, 1963). This method, besides permitting rapid and continuous measurements starting immediately after insemination, has the additional advantage that CO_2 does not interfere with the measurements. These investigators were thus able to show that coincident with the beginning of the elevation of the fertilization membrane, oxygen consumption increased rapidly, reached a maximum when the membrane had fully formed, and then rapidly decreased, reaching, however, a level that was considerably higher than that of the unfertilized egg. The change was complete in 2 to 3 minutes (Fig. 6–5).

This type of respiratory change is not the rule among animal eggs. Studies on eggs of a number of invertebrates and vertebrates have shown that in the eggs of only a few animals does an increase in respiration similar to that of the sea urchin egg occur. In others,

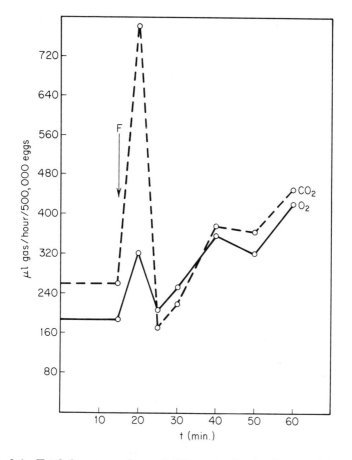

Fig. 6–4. Total O_2 consumption and CO_2 production by the egg of *Psammechinus miliaris* during the first hour following fertilization. *F*, addition of spermatozoa. (From Laser and Rothschild, 1939.)

no change has been detected for several hours after fertilization and in a few others even a temporary decrease has been reported.

The pertinent results are summarized in Table 4. The data in the table have been arranged according to the stage of maturation at which fertilization takes place. In fact, one possible explanation of the differences observed is that the direction of the respiratory change depends on the stage of maturation of the egg at which fertilization takes place, an increase only occurring when the egg

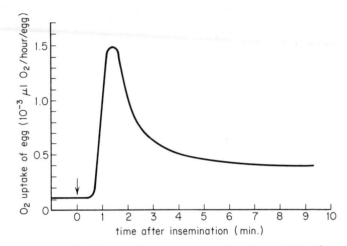

Fig. 6–5. Change in the rate of oxygen consumption of eggs of *Pseudocentrotus depressus* during the first 10 minutes following fertilization, measured polarographically. Arrow indicates addition of sperm. (From Ohnishi and Sugiyama, 1963.)

is fertilized after completion of maturation. This interpretation may be partly correct. Whitaker (1933b) had in fact already suggested that "the changes in rate of oxygen consumption at fertilization by different species of eggs, differing both in direction and magnitude, appear to be such as to bring the rate, when development is initiated, to about the same rate, which is also the rate of other comparable normally growing cells." This means that the previous history of the egg, that is, the events of its maturation, is directly responsible for the metabolic condition of the egg which causes the type of respiratory change that follows fertilization. This stresses again the need for a better understanding of the chemistry of maturation. A few additional words of comment on Table 4 are necessary. It must be noted that in most cases measurements were started quite a long time after fertilization—one hour or so—and hence any transient change which may have taken place *at* fertilization, such as that described in the sea urchin egg (Laser and Rothschild, 1939; Ohnishi and Sugiyama, 1963), has been missed.

In some other experiments the determinations have been biased by the peculiarity of the material itself, such as the formation of the large gel mass around the *Nereis* egg following fertilization,

Ratio of O_2 Uptake of Fertilized to that of Unfertilized Eggs[a]

Organism	Stage of maturation at the time of fertilization	$\dfrac{-O_2f}{-O_2u}$	Author
Nereis succinea	Germinal vesicle	1.3	Barron, 1932
Mactra laterialis		1.8	Ballantine, 1940
Urechis caupo		1.2	Tyler & Humason, 1937
Nereis limbata		1.35–1.45	Whitaker, 1931c
Asterias glacialis		1.0	Whitaker, 1933b
Cumingia tellinoides	Metaphase of the first maturation division	0.45	Whitaker, 1931b
Chaetopterus variopedatus		0.53	Whitaker, 1933a; Brachet, 1938
Marthasterias glacialis		1.0	Borei, 1948
Saxostrea commercialis		1.0	Cleland, 1950
Sabellaria alveolata		1.1	Fauré-Fremiet, 1922
Ciona intestinalis		1.0	Holter & Zeuthen, 1944
Ciona intestinalis		1.5	Tyler & Humason, 1937
Ciona intestinalis		2.0	Lentini, 1961
Phallusia mamillata		2.0	Lentini, 1961; Minganti, 1957
Rana platyrrhina	Metaphase of the second maturation division	1.0	Zeuthen, 1944
Bufo bufo		1.0	Stefanelli, 1938
Fundulus heteroclitus		16.7	Boyd, 1928
Fundulus heteroclitus		1.0	Philips, 1940
Oryzias latipes		1.0	Nakano, 1953
Fucus vesiculosus		1.9	Whitaker, 1931a
Strongylocentrotus purpuratus		3.7	Tyler & Humason, 1937
Psammechinus miliaris		3.6	Borei, 1948
Paracentrotus lividus		4.7	Brock, Druckerey & Herken, 1938
Arbacia punctulata		4.5	Ballantine, 1940
Dendraster excentricus		3.0	Tyler & Humason, 1937

[a] The ratio O_2 uptake, fertilized eggs ($-O_2f$) /O_2 uptake, unfertilized eggs ($-O_2u$) in various organisms ordered in groups according to the stage of maturation when fertilization takes place.
SOURCE: A table of Rothschild, 1956*, with additions.

which made it necessary to reduce the number of eggs in the manometer at the expense of accuracy (Whitaker, 1931c). There is also a puzzling discrepancy between the observations of Holter and Zeuthen (1944), who did not find any change in the respiratory rate following fertilization in the eggs of *Ciona intestinalis* collected in the North Sea, and those of Tyler and Humason (1937) and of Lentini (1961), who found an increase. The first explanation that comes to mind is that of technical differences, the observations of Holter and Zeuthen having been made with the Cartesian diver, and those of Tyler and Humason and Lentini with the conventional Warburg manometer. It is desirable that all these determinations be repeated under more accurately controlled experimental conditions: the polarographic method, as used by Ohnishi and Sugiyama (1963) could probably give the most precise answer. Of course, just as has been mentioned in connection with Borei's results (1948), the possibility that ecological conditions may influence the direction of the post-fertilization respiratory change of the egg cannot be ruled out. This, however, remains to be proved.

Attempts at identifying the significance of the respiratory changes

Mere description of changes in oxygen consumption does not tell very much: what is in fact important is to know how the changes are brought about.

Studies along these lines have thus far been confined to the sea urchin egg, but the few data available for other eggs show that extensive comparative studies may be very rewarding.

In the case of the sea urchin egg, a few facts have become known in recent times which help to explain how respiration is kept at a low level in the unfertilized egg, and also account for the sudden rise that follows fertilization.

The first important point is that in the unfertilized egg the concentration of ATP is quite high, whereas that of ADP is very low (Rossi *et al.*, personal communication). Since the availability of ADP is known to be one of the main limiting factors of respiration in cells (Lardy and Wellmann, 1952; Slater and Hülsman, 1957), its low concentration in the unfertilized egg will certainly result in a depression of respiration. Within a few minutes of fertilization, the ATP content drops from 1800 to about 1500 mμ

Moles/10^6 eggs; at the same time the ADP content increases from about 180 to 330 mμMoles (Fig. 6–6). Also Immers and Runnström (1960), studying the effect of dinitrophenol on the oxygen consumption of unfertilized and fertilized sea urchin eggs, had arrived at the conclusion that one of the limiting factors of respiration in the unfertilized egg may be the shortage of phosphate acceptors.

It has been known since the work of Örström and Lindberg (1940) and Lindberg (1943, 1945) that in the sea urchin egg within 10 minutes after fertilization there occurs a significant breakdown of a polysaccharide (tentatively indicated as glycogen). More recently, Monroy and Vittorelli (1960) demonstrated that a polysaccharide they had been able to prepare from unfertilized eggs was no longer obtainable from eggs within five minutes after fertilization. They further showed that at the same time the total "polysaccharide" fraction of the egg undergoes a 20-percent decrease without change in *total carbohydrates*. Now it has been found (Aketa *et al.*, 1964) that in the unfertilized egg the level of all glycolytic intermediates and of hexose phosphates is exceedingly low, a situation which strongly limits the oxidative breakdown of carbohydrates and respiration as a whole. This, together with the presence of large amounts of glycogenlike material, points to a

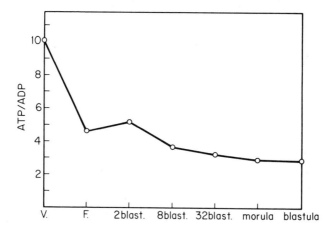

Fig. 6–6. Change in the ratio of ATP to ADP in the eggs of *Paracentrotus lividus* following fertilization and during early development. Value on the ordinate is that of the unfertilized eggs. *F*, eggs 30 minutes after fertilization. (Courtesy of Drs. Rossi, Aiello, and Scarano.)

block of the pathway leading from glycogen to glucose-6-phosphate. This block is released upon fertilization. Indeed, within 5 minutes after fertilization the level of the phosphate esters is greatly increased (Table 5). Hence, according to these findings, the increased rate of hexose phosphate synthesis, probably as a result of the activation of the hexose monophosphate shunt, may be involved in the rise of respiration that follows fertilization. That the shunt is the main pathway of glucose utilization in the sea urchin embryo was already known (Lindberg and Ernster, 1948; Keltch, Krahl, and Clowes, 1956; Krahl, 1956; Ghiretti and D'Amelio, 1956). One of the most important results of the activation of the shunt may be the increased level of TPNH. The concentration of this coenzyme in fact has been shown to increase during the first few hours of development both of *Arbacia* and of the mollusk *Spisula* (Krane and Crane, 1960). (See addendum 6–4.)

The interpretation suggested by Aketa *et al.* (1964) to explain the sudden formation of G-6-P following fertilization is that the phosphorlyase reaction, which seems to be the key step in regulating

Table 5

Concentration of Glucose-6-Phosphate (G-6-P), Fructose Diphosphate (F-dP) and Triosephosphate (Tri.P) in Unfertilized and newly Fertilized Eggs of *Arbacia lixula* and *Paracentrotus lividus*.[a]

		G-6-P	F-dP	Tr.P
Arbacia	Unfertilized	0.053		
	Fertilized 5 min	0.260		
	Unfertilized	0.055		
	Fertilized 10 min	0.470		
	Unfertilized	0.076	0.003	0.007
	Fertilized 10 min	0.166	0.014	0.023
Paracentrotus	Unfertilized		0.002	0.002
	Fertilized 5 min		0.039	0.043
	Unfertilized	0.068		
	Fertilized 8 min	0.456		
	Unfertilized	0.063		
	Fertilized 12 min	0.408		

[a] Values are expressed as μMoles/100 mg of total N of eggs.
Source: Aketa *et al.*, 1964.

glycogenolysis (Axelrod, 1960), is inhibited in the unfertilized egg, the inhibition being released upon fertilization. Whether or not such an activation actually occurs remains to be verified.

Aldolase (Ishihara, 1957, 1958a and b) and some enzymatic activities connected with the pentose phosphate cycle, such as glucose-6-phosphate dehydrogenase (Isono, 1963; Isono et al., 1963) and 6-phosphogluconate dehydrogenase (Bäckström, 1963) are also activated upon fertilization. In the case of aldolase, the observations of Ishihara indicate that in the unfertilized egg this enzyme is present in an inactive form, being bound to some cellular component; a few minutes after fertilization or artificial activation, the active enzyme is released into the soluble cytoplasmic fraction. Recent data of the same author (Ishihara, 1963) show that in the unfertilized egg the binding site may be the egg surface. Thus the release of the enzyme may somehow be connected with the surface changes. Also glucose-6-phosphate dehydrogenase in the unfertilized egg is bound to a fraction sedimenting at low speed, whereas 5 minutes after fertilization it is almost entirely recovered in the supernatant (Isono, 1963) (Fig. 6–7). In vitro experiments have shown that the release of the enzyme from its bound form may be brought about simply by increasing the ionic strength of the medium. When this is then lowered again, the enzyme becomes re-bound (Isono et al., 1963). The authors suggest a possible correlation with the release of K that also occurs upon fertilization (see below), as a mechanism to account for the release of the enzyme.

These observations therefore lead one to speculate that in the course of maturation inactivation of enzymes takes place through a process whereby they are prevented from interacting with their substrates. Such a spatial separation might occur in a number of ways and among others, through a binding of the enzyme to some cellular component (thus possibly resulting in a conformational change of the enzyme molecule), the process being reversed at fertilization. It would be interesting to verify this hypothesis.

It has been observed by Monné and Hårde (1952) that in the oocyte mitochondria are evenly dispersed in the cytoplasm, whereas in the mature egg they are mostly agglutinated in clumps. Electron microscopic pictures confirm this observation and further show that in the unfertilized egg the mitochondria are often clumped around

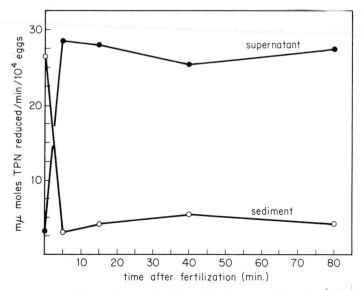

Fig. 6–7. Release of glucose-6-phosphate dehydrogenase from insoluble into soluble fraction upon fertilization in eggs of *Hemicentrotus pulcherrimus*. Sediment and supernatant from homogenates centrifuged at 24,000 g. (From data of Isono, 1963.)

lipid granules (Pasteels *et al.*, 1959). Soon after fertilization, mitochondria redisperse uniformly throughout the cytoplasm (Monné and Hårde, 1952). Whether or not the aggregated condition may influence the metabolic activity of the mitochondria is difficult to say, although it is not unlikely. An important contribution to the metabolic changes of the egg at fertilization might come from alterations of the mitochondrial membrane which would promote exchanges with the surrounding cytoplasm. There are in fact observations that provide some evidence that a change of some kind in the structure of the mitochondrial membrane actually takes place following fertilization. The extent to which mitochondria can swell in hypotonic media (as measured by the change in light absorption) was found to be decreased within 10 minutes after fertilization (Monroy, 1957a). In addition, electron micrographs of unfertilized and fertilized sea urchin eggs have shown that whereas in the former the mitochondria are dark, with cristae densely packed, in the latter they appear as if they had swollen; that is, they are much less electron dense, larger, and with cristae farther apart (Millonig, unpublished observations). It seems therefore likely that due to the metabolic changes taking place in the egg as a result of fertilization, mitochondria may undergo a swelling. That mitochondrial swelling and contraction are dependent on metabolic factors, and especially on respiration and oxidative phosphorylation, is now well established; there is evidence that they occur also during the functional cycles of the cell (Frédéric, 1958; see Lehninger, 1962, for a review). Therefore the fact that the mitochondria from fertilized eggs swell less in hypotonic media than those from unfertilized ones may depend on the former having already undergone a partial swelling in the egg.

The idea that in the unfertilized egg there might be a physical barrier preventing enzymes and substrates from interacting a barrier which is removed at fertilization, was first advanced by Runnström (1933). He had in fact suggested that in the unfertilized egg cytochrome oxidase is morphologically separated from cytochrome c, contact being established following fertilization. Furthermore, according to Runnström (see 1956), in the unfertilized egg cytochrome oxidase is relatively "unsaturated," and saturation progressively increases as development proceeds. Support for this view has come from experiments on the oxidation of CO to CO_2 by unfertilized and fertilized eggs (Black et al., 1958; Black and Tyler, 1959a and b). It was already known that CO stimulates the rate of oxygen consumption of sea urchin eggs (Runnström, 1930; Lindahl, 1938; Rothschild, 1949), of Urechis eggs (Rothschild and Tyler, 1958), and of ascidian eggs (Minganti, 1957). By using $C^{13}O$, Black et al. (1958) were able to show in the eggs of Urechis and Strongylocentrotus that this is due to the oxidation of the CO to CO_2, mediated by cytochrome oxidase. In the fertilized eggs the rate of this oxidation is higher in the light; but as development proceeds and the rate of oxygen consumption increases, CO utilization in the light diminishes while its inhibitory effect in the dark becomes stronger. The explanation suggested by Black and Tyler (1959b) is that while an acceleration of the electron transport by the cytochrome system increases the oxidation of CO, when this rate becomes very high, the oxidation of CO falls. In fact, according to Breckenridge (1953) inhibition of the cytochrome oxidase by combination with CO occurs if at least three of the four iron atoms of the cytochrome become reduced (in the presence of excess cytochrome c or of reducing substrates). These observations favor Runnström's view that the cytochrome system is progressively thrown into operation as development proceeds.

Almost coincident with the transient outburst of oxygen consumption, a transient production of an acid has been observed in the sea urchin egg (Ashbel, 1929; Runnström, 1933). The production of the acid was originally inferred from the displacement of CO_2 from the sea water. Attempts to identify the nature and the origin of the acid have given rise to considerable controversy. Runnström (1933) and Yčas (1954) did not find any significant increase either of lactic acid or of any of the intermediates of the Krebs cycle. However, Aketa (1957) has recently provided convincing evidence that a transient aerobic accumulation of lactic acid occurs *in some* sea urchin genera during the first few minutes after fertilization. In the Japanese sea urchin species investigated by this author, the increased rate of production of lactic acid occurred within 2 to 5 minutes after fertilization and then returned to the original prefertilization levels. The same is true in the Mediterranean species *Arbacia lixula* (Fig. 6–8A), whereas in the eggs of *Paracentrotus* (Fig. 6–8B) no change has been detected (thus confirming Runn-

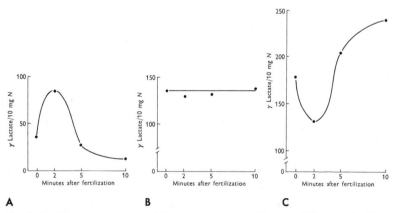

Fig. 6–8. Changes in lactic acid content in sea urchin eggs following fertilization. (A) Transient accumulation in the eggs of *Arbacia lixula*. (B) No change in the eggs of *Paracentrotus lividus*. (C) Transient decrease and subsequent recovery in *Psammechinus miliaris*. (From Aketa, 1964.)

ström's results on the same species). A peculiar situation occurs in the eggs of *Psammechinus miliaris* (Fig. 6–8C), of the Swedish west coast, in which there is a high concentration of lactic acid in the unfertilized egg. Within 2 minutes after fertilization, the concentration of lactic acid decreases, but the original value of the unfertilized egg (and in some batches an even higher one) is rapidly attained again. The significance of these species differences is obscure. The fact that in some species a momentary aerobic accumulation of lactic acid occurs may be taken as an indication of a very transient phase during which glycolysis is pre-eminent, whereas in the following development it becomes of very little if any importance.

According to Aketa, this lactic acid production has nothing to do with the "fertilization acid." Actually, Aketa (1963) has suggested, the fertilization acid may be a strong inorganic acid. He has found indeed a release of SO_4'' groups from the egg immediately following fertilization; these, according to the author, would derive from the breakdown of the sulfate-containing acidic mucopolysaccharides of the cortical granules. The failure to observe any acid production when the breakdown of the cortical granules is inhibited is evidence in favor of this view.

On the other hand, Mehl and Swann (1961) on the basis of titration experiments in the water in which sea urchin eggs were being fertilized, have come to the conclusion that the acid cannot be a weak acid (that is, an acid with pK between 3 and 8). From their calculations, Mehl and Swann concluded that at least one half of the fertilization acid is likely to depend on "the appearance in or on the egg of new acidic groups, which then release hydrogen ions into the medium. In addition there is good evidence that basic groups also are exposed." They favor the idea of "changes in the number or strength of acidic and basic ionizing groups attached to the egg, resulting from changes in the state of certain egg proteins." The metabolic origin of the acid would thus seem to be ruled out. However, Fujii and Ohnishi (1963) have suggested that the acid production may be due to the release of H^+ from the egg surface. They have formulated the hypothesis that fertilization triggers the breakdown of DPN with consequent liberation of H^+. This is likely to occur as a result of activation of DPNase which cleaves DPN at the nicotinamide-ribose linkage.

Clearly, the whole question of the nature and origin of the fertilization acid is still in a state of considerable confusion and further experiments would be welcome.

The suggestion that metabolic inhibitors may form and accumulate in the egg in the course of maturation has been repeatedly presented. As mentioned in Chapter Five, Runnström (1949) has indicated the surface of the mature egg as the site of an inhibitor-enzyme complex which on being split up upon fertilization is the sparking reaction of activation. More recently, Brachet (1960*) has suggested that unfertilized eggs may contain an inhibitor of cellular oxydations which the egg could get rid of thanks to the sudden increase in permeability that follows fertilization.

Brachet's hypothesis appeared almost at the same time as the announcement of the discovery of an inhibitor of cytochrome oxidase in the unfertilized egg (Maggio and Monroy, 1959; Maggio et al., 1960). It was observed that particulate-free extracts of unfertilized sea urchin eggs exert a strong inhibition on the activity of cytochrome oxidase, whereas the inhibition is almost entirely abolished in extracts of freshly fertilized eggs (Fig. 6–9). Some attempts at purifying and chemically defining the inhibitor have been made. The inhibitor is a heat- and alkali-labile, low molecular weight substance which acts by competitively interfering with the reoxidation of cytochrome oxidase. Its activity depends on the availability of $-SH$ groups, a finding that is in accord with the observed reversible inhibition of cytochrome oxidase by reagents reacting with disulfide bonds, such as reduced glutathione and cysteine (Cooperstein, 1963). The inhibition at the end of the chain of electron transport may impair the function of the whole system. How the inhibitor is released or inactivated upon fertilization is not known, nor have we any idea as to its location within the egg. It may be that the inhibitor is either extramitochondrial or easily diffusible from the mitochondria. In fact, mitochondria prepared from unfertilized or fertilized sea urchin eggs exhibit, in vitro, the same cytochrome oxidase activity (Maggio and Ghiretti-Magaldi, 1958; Maggio, 1959), and the same ability to incorporate amino acids into their proteins (Giudice, 1960).

The activation of protein synthesis

Fertilization is the beginning of morphogenesis, which consists fundamentally in the synthesis of new proteins.

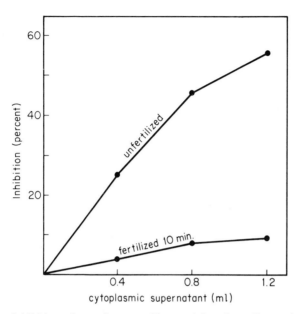

Fig. 6–9. Inhibition of cytochrome oxidase activity of rat liver mitochondria by different concentrations of 105,000 g cytoplasmic supernatant of unfertilized and fertilized eggs of *Paracentrotus lividus*. Both supernatants had the same concentration. (From Maggio and Monroy, 1959.)

In the egg which is ready for fertilization, protein synthesis occurs at a very low level, and is activated almost immediately following fertilization. This became clear from the first experiments in which unfertilized and fertilized eggs were exposed to radioactive amino acids or amino acid precursors. The experiments indicated that in the unfertilized egg the incorporation of labeled precursors into proteins is exceedingly small. However, also the rate of penetration into the egg is quite low. Following fertilization the rate of penetration is considerably increased, and at the same time incorporation into proteins begins (Hultin, 1950, 1952, 1953a, b; Hultin and Wessel, 1952, Hobermann *et al.*, 1952; Giudice *et al.*, 1962; Monroy and Vittorelli, 1962). Therefore one might suggest that the low rate of entry of the labeled precursors into the unfertilized egg was the rate-limiting factor of incorporation into proteins. However, experiments in which the amino acids of the pool were labeled under conditions which ruled out permeabil-

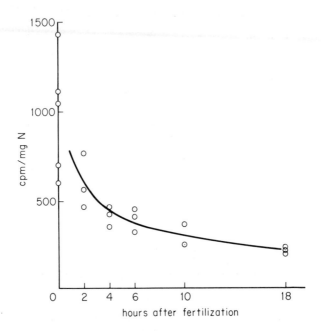

A

Fig. 6–10. Unfertilized eggs of *Paracentrotus lividus* were prelabeled with S^{35}-methionine by injection into the body cavity of the female: on the ordinate, radioactivity in the unfertilized eggs. The radioactivity of the TCA-soluble fraction decreases rapidly after fertilization (A) while at the same time it increases in the mitochondria (B). (From Nakano and Monroy, 1958a.)

ity factors proved that this is not so and that the unfertilized egg actually suffers from a block at some level of its protein synthesizing machinery.

In these experiments unfertilized sea urchin eggs were labeled in the gonad with radioactive methionine injected into the body cavity of the female (Nakano and Monroy, 1958a). The radioactivity was found to be almost entirely confined to the amino acid pool, whereas that in the proteins was negligible; the situation did not change appreciably as long as the egg remained unfertilized. A few minutes after fertilization, a lively incorporation into mitochondria (Fig. 6–10A, B) (Nakano and Monroy, 1958a), microsomes, and soluble proteins (Fig. 6–11) (Monroy, 1960) begins. The same result is obtained following butyric acid activation (Nakano *et al.*,

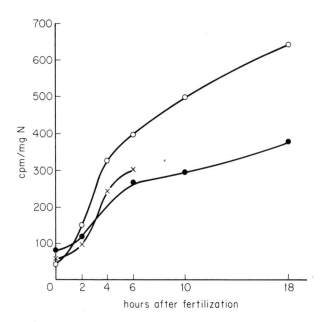

Fig. 6–10B.

1958). In such an experiment, permeability factors are ruled out and the evidence strongly points toward an intracellular block of protein synthesis. It was further shown that unfertilized eggs are able not only to metabolize amino acids, but also to synthesize amino acids from glucose; and yet the egg is unable to utilize the amino acids for protein synthesis. Thus S^{35}-methionine is rapidly used for the synthesis of glutathione (Nakano and Monroy, 1958b); when the egg is fertilized the radioactivity is transferred from glutathione to proteins. Also C^{14}-glucose is used by unfertilized eggs for the synthesis of C^{14}-alanine, serine, and glutamic and aspartic acid, but as long as the egg is unfertilized the radioactivity remains confined to the free amino acids of the pool (Monroy and Vittorelli, 1962). The same is true in the starfish egg (Monroy, unpublished).

Experiments with homogenates, in which permeability clearly does not play any role, showed that those from newly fertilized

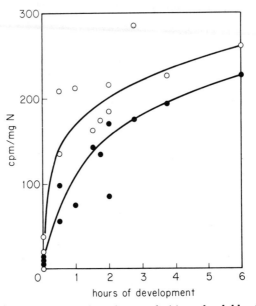

Fig. 6–11. Rapid labeling of the microsomal (o) and soluble (•) fractions following fertilization of *Paracentrotus* eggs. Experimental conditions as in Fig. 6–10. (From Monroy, 1960.)

eggs incorporate more than twice as much C^{14}-L-leucine into their proteins as homogenates from unfertilized eggs (Hultin and Bergstrand, 1960). These experiments also provided evidence that the difference is not due to a more efficient activation of the amino acids. Indeed, the situation was not changed either by fortifying the system with rat liver supernatant or by suspending the ribosomes from unfertilized eggs in rat liver supernatant. The presence of the amino acid activating enzyme system in the unfertilized egg had been recognized by Scarano and Maggio (1957), and it has now been shown that the enzyme system undergoes very little if any increase in activity until the blastula stage (Maggio and Catalano, 1963). Further experiments by Yasumasu and Koshihara (1963) (only a preliminary report in Japanese has been published thus far) have shown that the ability to synthesize amino acyl RNA is identical in homogenates of unfertilized or fertilized eggs. When, however, C^{14}-amino acyl RNA, from either unfertilized or fertilized eggs, was added to a cell-free system from unfertilized eggs, no incorporation into the proteins occurred; whereas a strong incorporation took place in a system from fertilized eggs. Thus these experiments strongly suggest that it is at the site of protein synthesis, that is, at the ribosomal level, that there is a gap in the protein-synthesizing machinery in the unfertilized egg. Direct proof of this was given when it was shown that ribosomes prepared from un-fertilized eggs have little ability to carry out *in vitro* incorporation of amino acids into proteins, whereas 30 minutes after fertilization incorporation is quite appreciable (Hultin, 1961). Hultin's interpre-tation of his result was that upon fertilization ribosomes undergo a structural rearrangement of some kind whereby they become "activated." Soon afterward, experiments from three different lab-oratories (Tyler, 1962, 1963; Nemer, 1962b; Wilt and Hultin, 1962; Nemer and Bard, 1963) showed that the ribosomes from unfertilized eggs can be stimulated *in vitro* by polyuridylic acid to synthesize polyphenylalanine. From these results it was concluded that the ribosomes of the unfertilized eggs are perfectly normal, but prob-ably it is the messenger RNA (mRNA) that is unavailable to the ribosomes. In fact, according to the messenger hypothesis, ribo-somes are unable to carry out protein synthesis until they receive the proper genetic information from the mRNA.

It was then shown that in the unfertilized egg by far the largest part of the ribosomal population is present in 73 S condi-tion (monosomes). Shortly after fertilization an increase in the per-centage of ribosomal aggregates (polysomes) is observed and these become more and more abundant as development proceeds. Pulse labeling with amino acids indicates that the incorporation is highest in the area of the polysomes (Monroy and Tyler, 1963) (Fig. 6–12A, B). Since it is now known that the major sites of protein synthesis in cells are clusters of ribosomes held together by molecules of mRNA (polysomes) (Warner *et al.*, 1962, 1963; Marks *et al.*, 1962, 1963; Weinstein *et al.*, 1963; Wettstein *et al.*, 1963; Staehelin *et al.*, 1963; Gierer, 1963; Gilbert, 1963; Noll *et al.*, 1963; Kiho and Rich, 1964), these observations appeared to support the conclusion that the mRNA is not available to the ribosomes in the unfertilized egg. The question is, how is mRNA made available to the ribosomes following fertilization? Evidently, the possible alternatives are (1) the messenger is already present in the unfertilized egg in a condition that prevents its activity, and this condition is changed as a result of activation; (2) the ribosomes of the unfertilized egg suffer from some structural defect (as suggested by Hultin, 1961)

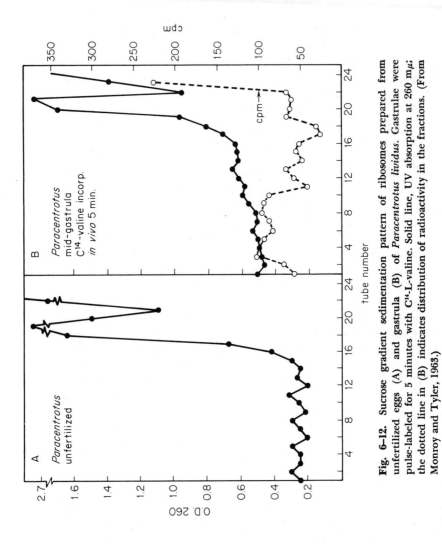

Fig. 6-12. Sucrose gradient sedimentation pattern of ribosomes prepared from unfertilized eggs (A) and gastrula (B) of *Paracentrotus lividus*. Gastrulae were pulse-labeled for 5 minutes with C^{14}-L-valine. Solid line, UV absorption at 260 mμ; the dotted line in (B) indicates distribution of radioactivity in the fractions. (From Monroy and Tyler, 1963.)

that prevents their combining with an otherwise normal mRNA; and (3) the mRNA is lacking altogether in the unfertilized egg, its synthesis beginning only after fertilization.

There is evidence that some nonribosomal, non-4 S RNA is synthesized by the egg very soon after fertilization (Gross and Cousineau, 1963, 1964; Nemer, 1963; Wilt, 1963; Gross et al., 1964). However, whether or not it may be described as mRNA is still uncertain. In fact, other possibilities may be considered, and in particular that this fraction is involved in the process of synthesis and maturation of ribosomes (see McCarthy et al., 1962; Britten et al., 1962).

There are two groups of observations that favor the hypothesis of the inactive mRNA store in the unfertilized egg. One is that actinomycin D (which is known to inhibit the DNA-dependent RNA synthesis), although causing a dramatic inhibition of RNA synthesis, does not inhibit protein synthesis during the period between fertilization and blastula. It is only after the blastula stage that protein synthesis is inhibited (Gross and Cousineau, 1963, 1964; Gross et al., 1964). The second and more cogent is that butyric acid activation stimulates protein synthesis in halves of sea urchin eggs enucleated (by centrifugation) before the activation (Brachet, Ficq, and Tencer, 1963; Denny and Tyler, 1964). In this case the possibility of a nuclear-dependent de novo synthesis of RNA is clearly ruled out, and the result weighs heavily in favor of the mRNA being present in the cytoplasm of the unfertilized egg in some condition, however, that makes it inactive. There is, however, one point that should be elucidated; that is the possible role of the DNA present in the cytoplasm.

The presence of an RNA in the unfertilized egg that can act in vitro as a template for protein synthesis has been shown by Maggio et al. (1964). In these experiments, total RNA extracted and purified from unfertilized sea urchin eggs was found to be able to stimulate incorporation of amino acids into proteins by rat liver ribosomes (Fig. 6–13). However, the same RNA preparations failed to stimulate incorporation by ribosomes of unfertilized sea urchin eggs, or only did so to a very small extent (thus confirming the findings of Wilt and Hultin, 1962, and of Brachet, Decroly, Ficq, and Quertier, 1963). Ribosomes from developmental stages instead could be stimulated. Hence, these experiments, although demon-

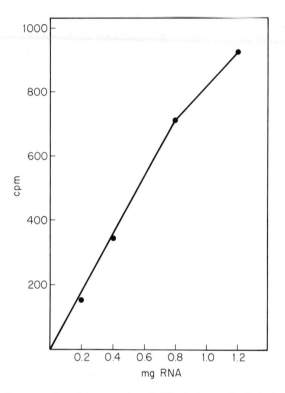

Fig. 6–13. Incorporation into proteins of C^{14} algal protein hydrolysate by rat liver ribosomes stimulated by various amounts of total RNA from unfertilized eggs of *Paracentrotus*. The RNA was added to the system after 8 minutes of preincubation and the incubation continued for 20 minutes. Incorporation without added RNA was subtracted from the counts of the RNA-containing samples. (From Maggio, *et al.*, 1964.)

strating that an RNA with messenger character is present in the unfertilized egg, at the same time indicate that also the ribosomes must be somehow abnormal. This of course does not rule out the additional possibility that the mRNA may be prevented from interacting with the ribosomes by being present in some condition that makes it inactive, a condition that might have been removed during the preparation and purification procedures. (See addendum 6–5.)

An important question is how the mRNA is protected from decay in the unfertilized egg. One possibility is that it may be made unavailable to the nucleases as a result of a conformational change or of a binding to some substance of high (cytoplasmic DNA?) or low molecular weight (histones?) within the egg. Vincent (1964) has suggested that the nucleolus produces a "messenger protector" protein having the function of protecting the messenger against destruction during its travel through the cytoplasm. This is particularly important in those cases in which the messenger has to spend some time in the cytoplasm.

Recent work has also shown that in bacteria in which protein synthesis has been stopped either with chloramphenicol or by subjection to anaerobiosis (that is, by depriving them of energy supply) the decay of the messenger is at least partially arrested (Fan *et al.*, 1964). Hence, the depression of the metabolism that occurs during maturation may account for the prevention of mRNA destruction and thus be responsible for the building up of its store.

Changes in distribution of ions and their effect on the egg metabolism

Changes in distribution of ions following fertilization may play an important part in all the metabolic events of fertilization. The transient increase in the rate of K^+ exchange coincident with the electrical changes at fertilization has already been mentioned. The behavior of K^+ has, however, some other interesting features. The concentration of K^+ inside the egg is about 17 times greater than in the sea water (see Chapter Four). Now, it has been shown that in the unfertilized egg only from one fifth to one sixth of K^+ is exchangeable, whereas after fertilization at least three fourths of it are readily exchangeable (Tyler and Monroy, 1959) (Fig. 6–14). The curves of K^+ uptake by unfertilized and fertilized eggs indicate that the difference cannot be accounted for by permeability changes.

It is interesting to note that in batches of eggs which for some reason were unresponsive to fertilization, the easily diffusible fraction was considerably greater (Monroy Oddo and Esposito, 1951). Furthermore the concentration of total K^+ has been found to change in a rhythmic fashion during the first cleavage (Monroy Oddo and Esposito, 1951).

This indicates a large-scale intracellular change in K^+ distribution at the time of fertilization, either as a result of a transition from the bound to a free state or as a result of changes in intracellular compartments. Now the stability of the ribosomes of the egg of

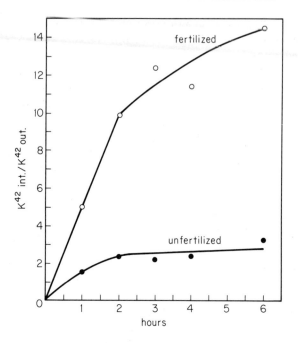

Fig. 6–14. Changes in the ratio of internal (K int.) to external (K out.) potassium in unfertilized and fertilized eggs of *Arbacia punctulata* placed in K^{42}-containing sea water. (Calculated from data of Tyler and Monroy, 1959.)

the echinoderm *Mellita quinquiesperforata* has been shown to be markedly dependent on K^+ (Ecker and Brookbank, 1963). In fact in the absence of K^+ the ribosomes tend to dissociate and Mg^{2+}, unless K^+ is present, causes the dissociation of the ribosomes into subunits. A dependence on K^+ for protein synthesis of the echinoderm ribosomes *in vitro* has also been demonstrated (Hultin, 1961).

The importance of ion-activated mechanisms has been demonstrated in the transformation of normal plant cells into crown gall tumors. In this case the change in the membrane permeability has been shown to play a most important role (Braun and Wood, 1962). Another interesting observation concerns the recently discovered effect of the Na to K ratio on the activation of the various genetic loci (as indicated by the appearance of puffs) in the chromosomes of the salivary glands of *Chironomus*. It has been suggested indeed that activation and inactivation of genetic loci "by progressive shifts of the Na^+/K^+ balance in the nuclear sap, may be a rather universal mechanism" (Kroeger, 1963).

Important changes in distribution and content of Ca^{2+} and Mg^{2+} have also been described in connection with fertilization. The pioneering work of Mazia (1937) indicated, in *Arbacia*, a release of Ca^{2+} from a bound to an ionic condition within 10 minutes after fertilization. Later work (Örström and Örström, 1942; Monroy Oddo, 1946) indicated that not only does a change in the binding of Ca^{2+} occur at fertilization, but also an actual loss. There was also a loss of Mg^{2+} by the egg during the first 10 minutes following fertilization (Monroy Oddo, 1946). Analyses of this type should, no doubt, be repeated with the more accurate methods available today; if confirmed, they would be of great significance for the interpretation of all the chemical events of fertilization.

Release of the metabolic inhibition in eggs fertilized before completion of maturation

The description given thus far refers largely to the sea urchin egg, which is fertilized after having completed the nuclear maturation. It would be interesting to learn something also about eggs in which fertilization occurs before the onset or completion of maturation. Since these eggs, too, suffer from a metabolic inhibition, an important question is whether the inhibition is released immediately upon fertilization—as in the sea urchin egg—or whether maturation must be completed first.

The only available data thus far refer to the initiation of protein synthesis in the starfish *Asterias forbesii* and in the mullusk, *Spisula solidissima*. The former egg is shed with the germinal vesicle intact, but maturation begins immediately and reaches completion (that is, the formation of the second polar body) independent of whether or not the egg is fertilized. In the latter, maturation (the breakdown of the germinal vesicle) is initiated by fertilization. In experiments on incorporation of labeled amino acids into proteins (Monroy and Tolis, 1964), it was found that in the *Asterias* eggs there is practically no difference between unfertilized and fertilized eggs until completion of maturation; but as soon as the second polar body has formed, the rate of incorporation increases rapidly in the fertilized eggs, whereas in the unfertilized eggs it does not change or even decreases (Fig. 6–15). In *Spisula* instead the great increase in the rate of incorporation begins a few minutes after the breakdown of the germinal vesicle and well before the formation of the first polar body (Fig. 6–16). These data are certainly too few to enable one to draw any significant conclusion. Among other things, one should know more about other aspects of metabolism and especially about the energy-yielding reactions. The investigations should furthermore be extended to as large a variety of eggs as possible. Nevertheless, one may tentatively suggest that in the eggs which are fertilized before nuclear maturation is completed, maturation must proceed to a certain stage (which is likely to be different in the different forms) for the release of inhibition to occur. This brings us back to the question discussed in the first section of this chapter, namely that of the role of the admixture of the nucleoplasm and the cytoplasm upon the breakdown of the germinal vesicle of the oocyte.

The activation of the nucleus

In the section of this chapter dealing with maturation, it has been postulated that the general inhibition of the metabolism of the egg is responsible for the arrest of nuclear maturation. This also means that the metabolism of the nucleus undergoes a depression in the course of maturation. The autoradiographic results of Ficq (1955, 1961) indicate a decline in the incorporation of nucleic acid precursors in the nucleus and in the nucleolus during the growth of the starfish oocyte. On the other hand, the observations of Gross and Cousineau (1963), Wilt (1963) and Gross et al. (1964) show the beginning of an RNA synthesis soon after fertilization; this seems to indicate that the nucleus, too, benefits from the release of the inhibition that follows fertilization. Indeed, one of the most important phenomena of the early post-fertilization stages of development, at least quantitatively, is DNA synthesis.

The investigations of Scarano (1958) and Scarano and Maggio (1959a, b) have now focused attention also on the possibility that the block of DNA synthesis in the unfertilized sea urchin egg may depend on the upset equilibrium of the deoxynucleotides in the pool, which in turn may depend on an unbalanced activity of the regulatory enzymes. In particular it may be that in the unfertilized egg the amino-pyrimidine-deoxynucleotide deaminase which converts the 5′-deoxycytidylic acid (dCMP) into 5-deoxyuridylic acid (dUMP) is more active than the dUMP reaminase system (observa-

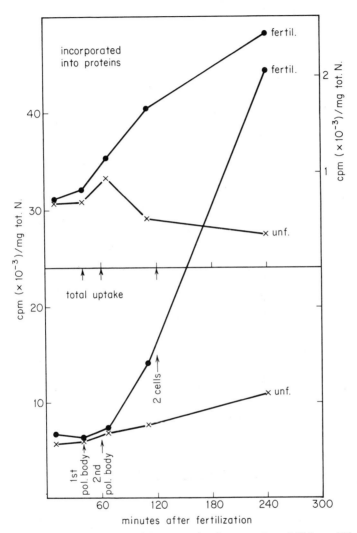

Fig. 6–15. Rate of entry and of incorporation into proteins of S^{35}-L-methionine in unfertilized and fertilized eggs of *Asterias forbesii*. Eggs pulse-labeled for 5 minutes. Figures on the left ordinate refer to the rate of entry and those on the right one to incorporation into proteins. (From Monroy and Tolis, 1964.)

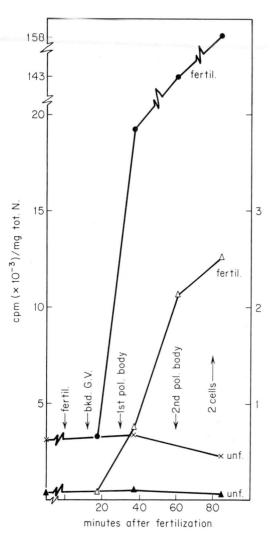

Fig. 6–16. Rate of entry (x———x: unfertilized eggs; ●———●: fertilized eggs) and of incorporation into proteins (▲———▲: unfertilized eggs; △———△: fertilized eggs) of L-Valine-1-C¹⁴ in eggs of *Spisula solidissima*. The eggs were pulse-labeled for 5 minutes. Values on the left ordinate refer to rate of entry and those on the right ordinate to incorporation into proteins. Here *Bkd. G. V.* stands for the point of breakdown of the germinal vesicle. (From Monroy and Tolis, 1964.)

tions by Scarano and Caserta, quoted by Scarano and Maggio, 1959b). This would result in an accumulation of dUMP in the pool, which not only upsets the nucleotide equilibrium of the pool, but, as shown by Nemer (1962a), is also very poorly utilized for the synthesis of thymidylic acid. It would be interesting to find out whether and when an activation of the dUMP reaminating enzyme(s) takes place following fertilization. This would result in re-establishing the deoxynucleotide equilibrium with the formation of the optimal amount of dCMP and of deoxythymidylate for DNA synthesis. Another important question concerns the time when the genetic material of the spermatozoon begins to participate in the synthesis of mRNA, and in particular whether or not that occurs before its fusion with the egg nucleus. However, we still know too little about when the paternal genome begins to manifest its effect. The results of Harding et al. (1954) show indeed that in sea urchin hybrids paternal-type antigens become detectable only at about the blastula stage. Here again we are not yet in a position to understand how nuclear activation is brought about.

Chemical and physical-chemical changes of the egg proteins

It was first shown by Mirsky (1936) that following fertilization there occurs a change in the physical chemical condition of some egg proteins. Mirsky found that within a few minutes after fertilization about 12 percent of the total protein of the egg becomes insoluble in 1 M KCl. The protein fraction that undergoes coagulation appeared to consist of exceedingly elongated particles. Mirsky suggested that the coagulation might be caused by the removal of the water shell around the protein particles, a view that is consistent with some recent interpretation of the changes occurring in the first stage of protein denaturation (see Klotz, 1958). This work was later extended in the writer's laboratory by the use of a number of different chemical and physical methods, and the results confirmed that modifications of some kind do occur in some of the egg proteins at fertilization. When extracts of unfertilized and fertilized eggs or fractions thereof were analyzed electrophoretically, considerable differences were found both in the number of components and in their mobility (Monroy, 1950; Monroy and Monroy Oddo, 1951, for the sea urchin eggs; Hamano, 1957, in the fish eggs). It is interesting to note that in the case of the fish egg, some of the changes observed in the newly fertilized egg could be duplicated by a gentle heating of extracts of unfertilized eggs (Hamano, 1957).

Further work concentrated on the fraction which is precipitated between 0 and 50 percent saturation with ammonium sulphate. This is certainly a complex mixture of several components (as indicated, for example, by electrophoretic analysis, D'Amelio 1955), and therefore results thus obtained may only be considered as a first approximation. As a result of fertilization this fraction becomes less susceptible to trypsin (D'Amelio, 1955; Giardina and Monroy, 1955) and when treated with urea reacts with a greater increase in viscosity and with a greater number of titrable phenolic groups than the same fraction from unfertilized eggs (Ceas, Impellizzeri, and Monroy, 1955). Also in extracts of newly fertilized fish eggs, an increased biuret reaction has been observed (Hamano, 1957). These results, however crude, strongly suggest a rearrangement of some kind in some of the egg proteins as a result of fertilization; they are strongly reminiscent of the changes occurring in proteins upon denaturation. There are indications that molecular rearrangements of some proteins also occur in the nerve fiber subjected to stimulation. In this case an unmasking of amino side-groups has been observed, and the change has been tentatively described as "reversible denaturation" (Ungar et al., 1957). One of the best known indications of protein denaturation is an increase in titrable −SH groups. Whether or not any such increase occurs at fertilization has been the subject of considerable dispute. Rapkine (1931) was the first to indicate an increase in −SH groups upon fertilization. Later work both confirmed (Bolognari, 1952) and refuted (Infantellina and La Grutta, 1948; see also Mazia, 1959) Rapkine's conclusion, until the question was cleared up by the work of Sakai and Dan (1959) and of Sakai (1960). This work has confirmed that between fertilization and the point just before the fusion of the pronuclei there occurs a decrease in titrable −SH groups followed by an increase. However, these authors have been able to show that the fluctuations depend on the interchange of −SH $\rightleftarrows$ −S−S− groups of one protein fraction soluble in trichloroacetic acid, but not on an unmasking of −SH groups. It is hard at the moment to say what the significance of this phenomenon may be. One possibility is that it may be related to the formation of the mitotic spindle of the first division (see Mazia, 1961*).

One possible interpretation of the mechanism whereby the changes in the proteins are brought about is that they may be the result of a proteolytic cleavage. In fact, in the sea urchin (Lundblad, 1949, 1950, 1952, 1954a, b; Lundblad and Lundblad, 1953; Maggio, 1957) and in the fish egg (Hamano, 1957), a transient increase of proteolytic activity has been observed immediately after fertilization (Fig. 6–17). Runnström (1949*) had already suggested that such a proteolytic attack may be responsible for the unmasking of important reactive groups of proteins, which would thus confer new properties on the proteins themselves. (See discussion in addendum 6–5.) That an important breakdown of some proteins occurs in conjunction with fertilization could have been inferred from the finding (Örström, 1941b; Ricotta, 1956) that the total non-protein amino-nitrogen undergoes an increase during the first 10 minutes after fertilization. The pioneering work of Örström (1941a) —the first thorough study of the metabolism of the fertilized sea urchin egg—indicated an accumulation of ammonia also during the first few minutes following fertilization (from 1.14 μMoles/g wet weight of unfertilized *Paracentrotus* eggs to 1.64 μMoles, 10 min after fertilization).

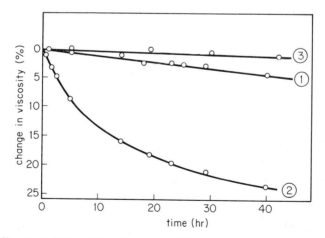

Fig. 6–17. Proteolytic activity of extracts of *Paracentrotus* eggs 3 minutes after fertilization (2) as compared to that of unfertilized eggs (1) and of eggs 30 minutes after fertilization (3) as measured from the viscosity-lowering effect on gelatin. (From Lundblad, 1949.)

Örström tried to trace the origin of ammonia and suggested that it might derive from hydrolysis of aminopurines. On the other hand, he was also able to demonstrate a simultaneous increase of glutamine (1.68 μMoles/g of eggs/10 min). One way to account for such an increase is a synthesis of glutamine from ammonia and glutamic acid (this synthesis could actually be shown to occur in fertilized but not in unfertilized eggs, incubated in the presence of glutamic acid and an ammonium salt). Another possibility was that it might derive from a proteolytic breakdown of proteins. It would be of great importance to repeat Örström's work taking advantage of the easier and more accurate methods available today.

By analogy with the ovalbumin → plakalbumin change (see Linderström-Lang, 1952) and with the processes leading to the activation of some enzymes—such as the conversion of pepsinogen to pepsin and of chymotrypsinogen to chymotrypsin—it has been suggested (Monroy, 1950, 1957b, 1957*) that the increased non-protein aminonitrogen may derive from the splitting off of some end groups of proteins. In all these cases the change is the result of proteolytic cleavage with release of one or more peptides, and the properties of the thus altered proteins are, as is known, very different from those of their precursors. In particular, they may be endowed with enzymatic properties while the precursor is not. To check the validity of this hypothesis one should (a) work with well-defined protein fractions and (b) identify the peptides or amino acids being released as a result of the proteolytic cleavage. This latter, however, may be a rather difficult proposition, as the proteolytic cleavage may affect only a small percentage of the total protein molecules of the egg, and hence the probability of identifying the released peptides or amino acids among the huge pool of the egg would be very small.

The above hypothesis may explain the shrinkage of most eggs at fertilization as being due to the volume changes accompanying proteolysis (see Linderström-Lang, 1952) and the resulting disarrangement of the water lattice around protein molecules (see Klotz, 1958). Also the density increase (from 1.068–1.088 to 1.091–1.095 g/ml; Salzen, 1957) of the sea urchin egg following fertilization may be accounted for by this hypothesis.

A transient or permanent volume change of the egg in conjunction with fertilization is quite a widespread occurrence. In some eggs, as in those of the polychaetes *Hydroides* and *Pomatoceros* (Monroy, 1954) and in the mammalian eggs (Austin, 1961*) a significant and permanent shrinkage occurs within a few minutes after fertilization. In the fish egg the decrease in volume ranges between 7 and 13 percent but may be accounted for as due to the extrusion of the content of the cortical alveoli (Yamamoto, 1961*).

In most sea urchin eggs there is probably no change in volume but only a temporary deformation. In the majority of eggs one can see a rapid wave of wrinkles which sweeps over the surface of the egg, starting from the point of entrance of the spermatozoon. In others, especially at the onset or towards the end of the spawning season, the deformation is quite marked; the egg then slowly acquires a spherical shape. These changes occur at the same time as the elevation of the fertilization membrane.

In the eggs of the ascidians the eggs respond to fertilization by exhibiting dramatic amoeboid movements which last for about 10 minutes (Reverberi, 1936). Similar movements have been described in the *Chaetopterus* egg (Lillie, 1906). Whether or not they fall within the same category as the volume changes is questionable.

Following fertilization, sea urchin eggs (Runnström, 1949*) and *Chaetopterus* eggs (Monroy, unpublished) become more opaque. In eggs drawn in glass capillaries, in which the fertilization impulse failed to propagate to the whole egg, the fertilized part of the egg appears more homogeneous than the unfertilized one (Allen and Hagström, 1955). A transient increase in opacity has been observed also in the axon of the nerve fiber during stimulation (Hill and Keynes, 1949).

It seems likely that these changes may all depend on the changed conditions of the egg proteins following fertilization. However, the available data are still too few and incomplete to allow a comprehensive view of the events.

ADDENDA

6–1. Measurements on highly homogeneous batches of maturing oocytes of *Asterias forbesii*, using the polarographic method, have shown that the rate of oxygen consumption remains constant throughout maturation (Horwitz, 1965).

HORWITZ, B. A., 1965. "Rates of oxygen consumption of fertilized and unfertilized *Asterias*, *Arbacia* and *Spisula* eggs." Exp. Cell Res. (in press).

6–2. Intense synthesis of RNA occurs during oogenesis in the toad, *Xenopus laevis* (Brown and Littna, 1964a and b). In particular, in the lampbrush phase, when the chromosomes are considered to be in a state of intense genetic activity, 90 percent or more of the RNA synthesized is of ribosomal type (Davidson *et al.*, 1964). At the onset of maturation this synthesis ceases while a small synthesis of heterogeneous RNA can still be detected. No further synthesis of ribosomal RNA takes place until the gastrula stage, whereas synthesis of heterogeneous, DNA-like RNA is found during cleavage (Brown and Littna, 1964 a). These observations thus throw additional light on the importance of the events of oogenesis. They show indeed that in the first part of embryonic development protein synthesis (and probably *all* protein synthesis) is carried out on the ribosomes synthesized during oogenesis.

BROWN, D. D., and LITTNA, E., 1964. "RNA synthesis during development of *Xenopus laevis,* the South African clawed toad," *J. Mol. Biol.*, 8: 669–687.
———, ———, 1964. "Variations in the synthesis of stable RNA's during oogenesis and development of *Xenopus laevis,*" J. Mol. Biol., 8: 688–695.
DAVIDSON, E., ALLFREY, V. G., and MIRSKY, A. E., 1964. "On the RNA synthesized during the lampbrush phase of amphibian oogenesis," *Proc. Nat. Acad.*, 52: 501–508.

6–3. Also in the starfish (*Asterias forbesii*) egg, fertilization is accompanied by a transient increase of the rate of oxygen consumption coincident with membrane formation. Starfish eggs can be fertilized at any time during the maturation process; that is, until the formation of the second polar body. The transient respiratory change has been found to occur no matter at which time during the maturation cycle the egg was fertilized. Respiration then returns to the prefertilization level and does not change at least until the first cleavage. No change at all occurs in the respiratory rate of the egg of the surf clam, *Spisula solidissima*, which, however, does not form fertilization membrane (Horwitz, 1965).

6–4. Recent work has demonstrated that in the sea urchin egg a three- to fivefold increase of TPNH occurs within 30 to 40 seconds after fertilization. The increase occurs at the expense of DPN that during the same period undergoes a parallel decrease. It is suggested that the enzyme involved in the reaction, the DPN-kinase, is activated upon fertilization (Epel, 1964 a). The formation of TPNH begins a few seconds *before* the onset of the respiratory change and examination of the experimental data shows that the increase in respiration may indeed be accounted for as due to an increased utilization of ATP for the formation of TPN and TPNH from DPN (Epel, 1964 b).

EPEL, D., 1964. "A primary metabolic change of fertilization: interconversion of pyridine nucleotides," *Bioch. Bioph. Res. Comm.,* **17**: 62–68.
——, 1964. "Simultaneous measurements of TPNH formation and respiration following fertilization of the sea urchin egg," *Bioch. Bioph. Res. Comm.,* **17**: 69–73.

6–5. Slight and irregular activations of ribosomes from unfertilized sea urchin eggs have been obtained by treatments known to be effective in causing parthenogenetic activation of the egg (butyric acid, Hultin, 1961; heating, Maggio, unpublished). On the other hand, consistent and strong activation is brought about by trypsin. As a result of such a treatment, ribosomes from unfertilized eggs acquire the ability to be stimulated by natural messenger RNA's while the response to poly-U becomes at least five times stronger. Furthermore, the ribosomes are now able to carry out *in vitro* incorporation of amino acids into proteins even in the absence of any exogenous RNA (Maggio *et al.,* 1965). It had been previously found (Maggio *et al.,* 1964) that the RNA faction of the unfertilized egg which is endowed with the ability to stimulate *in vitro* incorporation of amino acids into proteins (by ribosomes of rat liver or sea urchin embryos) is the one extracted from the ribosomes. Sucrose gradient fractionations indicated that the active component sediments with the 28 S fraction. It may be suggested that in the course of oogenesis the messenger RNA goes indeed to the ribosomes but it is then prevented from acting by the binding to a protein. The proteolytic enzyme that is activated upon fertilization (Lundblad, 1949, 1950) may be instrumental in removing the inhibitory protein.

MAGGIO, R., RINALDI, A. M., VITTORELLI, M. L., and MONROY, A., 1965. "Activation *in vitro* des ribosomes des oeufs vierges d'oursin," *C. R. Acad. des Sciences,* Paris (in press).

chapter seven

Some Concluding Remarks

I shall try now to sum up some of the more significant facts discussed in the previous chapters and to see whether and how they lend themselves to further development. On the other hand I shall try to avoid the "occupational disease" of the students of fertilization (Rothschild, 1956*), namely that of presenting a "theory of fertilization."

One of the most significant recent discoveries in the field of fertilization has certainly been that of the acrosome reaction, which has provided a morphological and physiological basis for the understanding of the egg-sperm interactions. The beautiful work of the Colwins has indicated how rewarding the morphological approach may still be and to what extent comparative studies may be illuminating. These studies have led to the important discovery concerning the method whereby the nuclear material of the spermatozoon is injected into the egg, a mechanism that has turned out to be strikingly similar to that of the injection of the phage DNA into the bacterium. Although more data should be collected before any general conclusion can be drawn, one cannot help thinking that penetration of one cell by another always takes place by means of a common fundamental mechanism, that of a specific membrane fusion. The study of specificity in the sperm-egg interaction may hence provide data of a more general biological significance. It might indeed be a convenient system to investigate the genetic control of structure and function of cell membranes. It is anticipated that immunological studies may provide data of the utmost importance.

Besides being the site of such interaction, the egg surface has been considered as the site of origin of the sparking reaction of activation. This is indeed a widely accepted view, but the substantiating evidence is only circumstantial.

The impact of the discoveries about protein synthesis and its controlling mechanisms has made itself felt in the field of embryology. On the other hand, embryological problems have started to attract the attention of biochemists, since the body of biochemical and genetical information already available makes one feel confident that an attack on these challenging problems may now be rewarding.

Fertilization marks the zero time of differentiation, and it therefore stands out as one of the most interesting aspects of the whole process. And indeed, it is possible that the study of fertilization may also contribute to our understanding of the controlling mechanisms of gene activity.

There is no question but that the most important result of fertilization is the release of the inhibition of the egg nucleus. How is such activation or de-repression accomplished? And how soon after fertilization does the genetic system of the zygote nucleus begin to send specific coding messages? We do know of a few genetic systems which are activated very soon after fertilization, as for example, the suppressor of erupt locus in *Drosophila*, which is activated within a few minutes after fertilization (Glass and Plaine, 1950). Another interesting case is that of the control of the rise of respiration of *Drosophila* eggs which begins soon after fertilization and fails to occur in the nullo-X mutants (Boell and Poulson, 1939). While the former case indicates very early formation of specific messages (synthesis of specific messenger?), the latter is suggestive of a direct nuclear control of some metabolic events. However, we do not know what the chemical mechanisms are whereby the activation is accomplished, and study of fertilization may hence throw some light on one of the most fundamental problems of differentiation, namely that of the turning on and off of gene activity. In the sea urchin egg there is evidence of a DNA-dependent RNA synthesis beginning very soon after fertilization. However, one may wonder whether this early RNA synthesis might not be directed by cytoplasmic DNA. The DNA cytoplasmic store is indeed another most peculiar and interesting feature of all eggs. That it is but a store to be utilized for the multiplication of nuclei during early cleavage seems a far too simplified—although admittedly quite possible—interpretation.

Too little is known about such cytoplasmic DNA, but the possibility that it may serve a genetic function during the early post-fertilization stages is very attractive and well worth investigating (see also Brachet, 1961*).

A new and probably decisive step forward in the study of fertilization will be made when more is known about the chemical events of maturation. The condition of the mature egg is the result of the long series of events which have taken place during maturation. It is indeed during maturation that the metabolic inhibition, one of the main features of the mature egg, builds up. Recent work has directed attention to a most important mechanism of regulation of enzyme activity in the cell, namely the allosteric transition (Monod *et al.*, 1963). One may wonder whether the metabolic inhibition which sets in during maturation may not be caused largely by the production and accumulation of allosteric effectors. Discovery of the mechanism of how the inhibition forms may help greatly to reveal how it is removed upon fertilization. This is actually the central problem of fertilization; thus far we have no idea which is the first reaction that sets in motion the chain of events responsible for the activation of the enzymatic machinery of the egg. Nor do we know how far from this sparking reaction are all the known chemical changes which are said to occur "at fertilization." There will be work for years to come to solve these problems.

References

Books and Reviews

*Books and reviews (these references are marked in the text with an asterisk *)*

AUSTIN, C. R., 1961. *The mammalian egg*, Oxford: Blackwell Scientific Publications, 183 pp.

———, and BISHOP, M. W. H., 1957. "Fertilization in mammals," *Biol. Rev.*, 32: 296–349.

BRACHET, J., 1945. *Embryologie chimique*, Paris: Masson et Cie., 531 pp.

———, 1957. *Biochemical cytology*, New York: Academic Press, 516 pp.

———, 1960. *The biochemistry of development*, New York: Pergamon Press, 320 pp.

COLWIN, A. L. and COLWIN, L. H., 1964. "Role of the gamete membranes in fertilization," pp. 233–279 in M. Locke, Ed. *Symp. on Cellular Membranes in Development*, New York: Academic Press.

DAN, J. C., 1956. "The acrosome reaction," *Internatl. Rev. of Cytol.*, 5: 365–393.

DORFMAN, W. A., 1963. *Physico-chemical foundations of fertilization*, Acad. Sci. of USSR, 255 pp. (in Russian)

LILLIE, F. R., 1919. *Problems of fertilization*, Chicago: University of Chicago Press, 278 pp.

LOEB, J., 1913. Artificial parthenogenesis and fertilization, Chicago: University of Chicago Press, 312 pp.

MAZIA, D., 1961. "Mitosis and the physiology of cell division," pp. 77–412 in J. Brachet and A. E. Mirsky, eds., *The Cell*, Vol. 3, New York: Academic Press.

METZ, CH. B., 1957. "Specific egg and sperm substances and activiation of the egg," pp. 23–69 in A. Tyler, R. C. von Borstel and Ch. B. Metz, eds., *The Beginnings of Embryonic Development*, Washington, D.C.: American Assoc. for the Advancement of Science.

METZ, CH. B., 1956. "Mechanisms in fertilization," *Physiol. Triggers*, pp. 17–45.

MINGANTI, A., 1958. "Sulla costituzione chimica degli involucri ovulari negli animali," *Boll. Zool.*, 25: 55–89.

121

MONROY, A., 1957. "An analysis of the process of fertilization and activation of the egg," *Internatl. Rev. of Cytol.*, **6**: 107–127.

——, in press. "Biochemical aspects of fertilization," pp. —— in R. Weber (ed.), *Biochemical aspects of development*, New York: Academic Press.

ROTHSCHILD, LORD, 1954. "Polyspermy." *Quart. Rev. of Biol.*, **29**: 332–342.

——, 1956. *Fertilization*, London: Methuen & Co., 170 pp.

——, 1958. "Fertilization in fish and lampreys," *Biol. Rev.*, **33**: 372–392.

RUNNSTRÖM, J., 1949. "The mechanism of fertilization in Metazoa," *Adv. in Enzymol.*, **9**: 241–328.

TYLER, A., 1941. "Artificial parthenogenesis," *Biol. Rev.*, **16**: 291–336.

——, 1948. "Fertilization and immunity," *Physiol. Rev.*, **28**: 180–219.

WARBURG, O., 1911. *Ueber die Oxydationen in lebenden Zellen nach Versuchen am Seeigelei*, Heidelberg: Rössler & Herbert, 38 pp.

WILSON, E. B., 1895. *An atlas of the fertilization and karyokinesis of the ovum*, New York: Columbia University Press and The Macmillan Co., 32 pp.

——, 1906. *The cell in development and inheritance*, 2nd ed., New York: The Macmillan Co., 483 pages.

YAMAMOTO, T., 1961. "Physiology of fertilization in fish eggs," *Internatl. Rev. of Cytol.*, **12**: 361–405.

Special articles

ADAMS, C. E., and CHANG, M. C., 1962. "Capacitation of rabbit spermatozoa in the Fallopian tube and uterus," *J. Exp. Zool.*, **151**: 159–165.

AFZELIUS, B. A., 1956. "The ultrastructure of the cortical granules and their products in the sea urchin egg as studied with the electron microscope," *Exptl. Cell Res.*, **10**: 257–285.

AKETA, K., 1957. "Quantitative analyses of lactic acid and related compounds in sea urchin eggs at the time of fertilization," *Embryologia*, **3**: 267–278.

——, 1963. "Studies on the acid production at fertilization of sea urchin eggs," *Exptl. Cell Res.*, **30**: 93–97.

——, 1964. "Some comparative remarks on the transient change in lactic acid content in sea urchin eggs following fertilization," *Exptl. Cell Res.*, **34**: 192–194.

——, BIANCHETTI, R., MARRÉ, E., and MONROY, A., 1964. "Hexose monophosphate level as a limiting factor for respiration in unfertilized sea urchin eggs," *Biochim. Biophys. Acta*, **86**: 211–215.

ALLEN, R. D., 1954. "Fertilization and activation of sea urchin eggs in glass capillaries," *Exptl. Cell Res.*, **6**: 403–424.

——, and HAGSTRÖM, B., 1955. "Interruption of the cortical reaction by heat," *Exptl. Cell Res.*, **9**: 157–167.

ALLFREY, V. G., MEUDT, R., HOPKINS, J. W., and MIRSKY, A. E., 1961. "Sodium dependent 'transport' reactions in the cell nucleus and their role in protein and nucleic acid synthesis," *Proc. Natl. Acad. Sci.*, **47**: 907–932.

ASHBEL, R., 1929. "La glicolisi nelle uova di riccio di mare fecondate e non fecondate," *Boll. Soc. Biol. Sper.*, **4**: 492–493.

Austin, C. R., 1956. "Cortical granules in hamster egg," *Exptl. Cell Res.*, 10: 533–540.

———, 1963. "Acrosome loss from the rabbit spermatozoon in relation to entry into the egg," *J. Reprod. Fertil.*, 6: 313–314.

———, and Amoroso, E. C., 1959. "The mammalian egg," *Endeavour*, 18: 130–143.

———, and Bishop, M. W. H., 1958a. "Some features of the acrosome and perforatorium in mammalian spermatozoa," *Proc. Roy. Soc. London*, B, 148: 234–240.

———, ———, 1958b. "Role of the rodent acrosome and perforatorium in fertilization," *Proc. Roy. Soc. London*, B, 149: 241–248.

Axelrod, B., 1960. "Glycolysis," pp. 97–128 in D. M. Greenberg (ed.), *Metabolic Pathways*, Vol. I, New York: Academic Press.

Bäckström, S., 1963. "6-Phosphogluconate dehydrogenase in sea urchin embryos," *Exptl. Cell Res.*, 32: 566–569.

Balinsky, B. J., 1960. "The role of cortical granules in the formation of the fertilization membrane and the surface membrane of fertilized sea urchin eggs," pp. 205–219 in S. Ranzi (ed.), *Symp. on the Germ Cells and Earliest Stages of Development*, Pallanza.

Ballantine, R., 1940. "Analysis of the changes in respiratory activity accompanying fertilization of marine eggs," *J. Cell. Comp. Physiol.*, 15: 217–232.

Banta, A. M., and Gartner, R. A., 1914. "A milky white amphibian egg jelly," *Biol. Bull.*, 27: 259–261.

Barron, E. S. G., 1932. "The effect of anaerobiosis on the egg and sperms of sea urchin, starfish and *Nereis* and fertilization under anaerobic conditions," *Biol. Bull.*, 62: 42–45.

Berg, W. E., 1950. "Lytic effects of sperm extracts on the eggs of *Mytilus edulis*," *Biol. Bull.*, 98: 128–138.

Bernstein, G. S., 1952. "Sperm agglutinins in the egg jelly of the frogs *Rana pipiens (Schreber)* and *Rana clamitans (Latreille)*," *Biol. Bull.*, 103: 285.

Bielig, H. J., and Dohrn, P., 1950. "Zur Frage der Wirkung von Echinochrome A und Gallerthüllensubstanz auf die Spermatozoen des Seeigels *Arbacia lixula*," *Ztsch. f. Naturf.*, 5b: 316–338.

Bishop, D. W., 1951. "Chromatographic analysis of fertilizin from the sand dollar, *Echinarachnius parma*," *Biol. Bull.*, 101: 215.

———, and Metz, Ch. B., 1952. "Fructose as a carbohydrate constituent of fertilizin from the sand dollar, *Echinarachnius parma*," *Nature*, 169: 548.

———, and Tyler, A., 1956. "Fertilizin of mammalian eggs," *J. Exp. Zool.*, 132: 575–602.

Black, R. E., and Tyler, A., 1959a. "Effects of fertilization and development on the oxidation of carbon monoxide by eggs of *Strongylocentrotus* and *Urechis* as determined by use of C^{13}," *Biol. Bull.*, 117: 443–453.

———, ———, 1959b. "Cytochrome oxidase and oxidation of CO in eggs of the sea urchin *Strongylocentrotus purpuratus*," *Biol. Bull.*, 117: 454–457.

————, EPSTEIN, S., and TYLER, A., 1958. "The oxidation of carbon monoxide by fertilized eggs of *Urechis caupo* shown by use of a C^{13} label," *Biol. Bull.*, 115: 153–161.

BOELL, E. J., and POULSON, D. F., 1939. "The respiratory metabolism of normal and genetically deficient eggs of *Drosophila melanogaster*," *Anat. Rec.*, 75, suppl. 1: 65.

BOLOGNARI, A., 1952. "Variazioni quantitative del contenuto in glutatione nelle uova fecondate di *Paracentrotus lividus*," *Arch. Sc. Biol.*, 36: 40–47.

BOREI, H., 1948. "Respiration of oocytes, unfertilized eggs and fertilized eggs from *Psammechinus* and *Asterias*," *Biol. Bull.*, 95: 124–150.

————, 1949. "Independence of post-fertilization respiration in the sea urchin egg from the level of respiration before fertilization," *Biol. Bull.*, 96: 117–122.

————, and LYBING, S., 1949. "Oxygen uptake of *Asterias* embryos before hatching," *Nature*, 163: 451–452.

BOVERI, T., 1888. "Ueber partielle Befruchtung," *Ber. Naturforsch. Ges. Freiburg i. Br.* 4: 64–72.

————, 1895. "Ueber das Verhalten der Centrosomen bei der Befruchtung des Seeigel-Eies nebst allgemeinen Bemerkungen über Centrosomen und Verwandtes," *Verh. phys. med. Ges. Würzburg*, 29: 1–75.

BOYD, M., 1928. "A comparison of the oxygen consumption of unfertilized and fertilized eggs of *Fundulus heteroclitus*," *Biol. Bull.*, 55: 92–100.

BRACHET, J., 1938. "The oxygen consumption of artificially activated and fertilized *Chaetopterus* eggs," *Biol. Bull.*, 74: 93–98.

————, DECROLY, M., FICQ, A., and QUERTIER, J., 1963. "Ribonucleic acid metabolism in unfertilized and fertilized sea urchin eggs," *Biochim. Biophys. Acta*, 72: 660–662.

————, FICQ, A., and TENCER, R., 1963. "Amino acid incorporation into proteins of nucleate and anucleate fragments of sea urchin eggs: effect of parthenogenetic activation," *Exptl. Cell Res.*, 32: 168–170.

————, and QUERTIER, J., 1963. "Cytochemical detection of cytoplasmic deoxyribonucleic acid (DNA) in amphibian oocytes," *Exptl. Cell Res.*, 32: 410–413.

BRADEN, A. W. H., 1952. "Properties of the membranes of rat and rabbits eggs," *Austral. J. Sci. Res.*, B 5: 460–471.

————, AUSTIN, C. R., and DAVID, H. A., 1954. "The reaction of zona pellucida to sperm penetration," *Austral. J. Biol. Sci.*, 7: 391–409.

BRAUN, A. C., and WOODS, H. N., 1962. "On the activation of certain essential biosynthetic systems in cells of *Vinca rosea L.*," *Proc. Natl. Acad. Sci.*, 48: 1776–1782.

BRECKENRIDGE, B., 1953. "Carbon monoxide oxidation by cytochrome oxidase in muscle," *Amer. J. Physiol.*, 173: 61–69.

BRITTEN, R. J., McCARTHY, B. J., and ROBERTS, R. B., 1962. "The synthesis of ribosomes in *E. coli*. 4. The synthesis of ribosomal protein and the assembly of ribosomes," *Biophys. J.*, 2: 83–93.

BROCK, N., DRUCKREY, H., and HERKEN, H., 1938. "Der Stoffwechsel des geschädigten Gewebes. III," *Arch. exper. Pathol. Pharmak.*, **188**: 451–464.

BROOKBANK, J. W., 1958. "Dispersal of the gelatinous coat material of *Mellita quinquiesperforata* eggs by homologous sperm and sperm extracts." *Biol. Bull.* **115**: 74–80.

BROOKS, S. C., 1939. "Intake and loss of radioactive cations by certain marine eggs," *Proc. Soc. Exp. Biol. Med.*, **42**: 557–558.

CEAS, M. P., IMPELLIZZERI, M. A., and MONROY, A., 1955. "The action of urea on some proteins of the unfertilized and fertilized sea urchin egg," *Exptl. Cell Res.*, **9**: 366–369.

CHAMBERS, E. L., 1939. "The movement of the egg nucleus in relation to the sperm aster in the echinoderm egg," *J. Exp. Biol.*, **16**: 409–424.

CHAMBERS, R., 1930. "The manner of sperm entry in the starfish egg," *Biol. Bull.*, **58**: 344–369.

———, 1933. "The manner of sperm entry in various marine ova," *J. Exp. Biol.*, **10**: 130–141.

CLELAND, K. W., 1950. "Respiration and cell division in developing oyster eggs," *Proc. Linnean Soc. N. S. Wales*, **75**: 282–295.

CLOWES, G. H. A., and BACHMAN, E., 1921. "On a volatile sperm-stimulating substance derived from marine eggs," *J. Biol. Chem.*, **46**: XXXI–XXXII.

COLE, K. S., 1938. "Electric impedance of marine egg membranes," *Nature*, **141**: 79.

———, and SPENCER, J. M., 1938. "Electric impedance of fertilized Arbacia egg suspensions," *J. Gen. Physiol.*, **21**: 583–590.

COLWIN, A. L., and COLWIN, L. H., 1955. "Sperm entry and the acrosome filament *(Holothuria atra* and *Asterias amurensis),*" *J. Morphol.*, **97**: 543–568.

———, ———, 1958. "Some characterization of the egg membrane lytic agent derived from sperm extracts of *Hydroides hexagonus,*" *Biol. Bull.*, **115**: 348.

———, ———, 1960. "Egg membrane lytic activity of sperm extract and its significance in relation to sperm entry in *Hydroides hexagonus* (Annelida)," *J. Bioph. Bioch. Cytol.*, **7**: 321–328.

———, ———, 1961. "Changes in the spermatozoon during fertilization in *Hydroides hexagonus* (Annelida). 2. Incorporation with the egg," *J. Bioph. Bioch. Cytol.*, **10**: 255–274.

———, ———, 1963. "Role of the gamete membranes in fertilization in *Saccoglossus kowalevskii* (Enteropneusta). 1. The acrosomal region and its changes in early stages of fertilization," *J. Cell Biol.*, **19**: 477–500.

———, ———, and PHILPOTT, D. E., 1957. "Electron microscope studies of early stages of sperm penetration in *Hydroides hexagonus* (Annelida) and *Saccoglossus kowalevskii* (Enteropneusta)," *J. Bioph. Bioch. Cytol.*, **3**: 489–502.

COLWIN, L. H., and COLWIN, A. L., 1956. "The acrosome filament and sperm entry in *Thyone briareus* (Holothuria) and *Asterias,*" *Biol. Bull.*, **110**: 243.

———, ———, 1960. "Formation of sperm entry holes in the vitelline membrane of *Hydroides hexagonus* (Annelida) and evidence of their lytic origin," *J. Bioph. Bioch. Cytol.*, **7**: 315–320.

————, ————, 1961. "Changes in the spermatozoon during fertilization in *Hydroides hexagonus* (Annelida). 1. Passage of the acrosomal region through the vitelline membrane," *J. Bioph. Bioch. Cytol.*, 10: 231–254.

————, ————, 1963. "Role of the gamete membranes in fertilization of *Saccoglossus kowalevskii* (Enteropneusta). II. Zygote formation by gamete membrane fusion," *J. Cell Biol.*, 19: 501–518.

CONKLIN, E. G., 1901. "Centrosome and sphere in the maturation, fertilization and cleavage of *Crepidula*," *Anat. Anz.*, 19: 280–287.

COOPERSTEIN, S. J., 1963. "Reversible inactivation of cytochrome oxidase by disulfide bond reagents," *J. Biol. Chem.*, 238: 3606–3610.

CORNMAN, J., 1941. "Sperm activation by *Arbacia* egg extracts, with special relation to echinochrome," *Biol. Bull.*, 80: 202–207.

CORRIAS, L., and NOVARINI, L., 1950. "Attivazione e agglutinazione di spermi di toro ad opera del liquido follicolare," *Mon. Zool. Ital.*, 57: 94–97.

COSTELLO, D. P., 1940. "The fertilization of nucleated and non-nucleated fragments of centrifuged *Nereis* eggs," *J. Morphol.*, 66: 99–114.

D'AMELIO, V., 1955. "Trypsin sensitivity of some proteins of the sea urchin egg before and after fertilization. An electrophoretic analysis," *Experientia*, 11: 443–445.

DAN, J. C., 1950a. "Sperm entrance in echinoderms, observed with the phase contrast microscope," *Biol. Bull.*, 99: 399–411.

————, 1950b. "Fertilization in the medusan, *Spirocodon saltatrix*," *Biol. Bull.*, 99: 412–415.

————, 1952. "Studies on the acrosome. 1. Reaction to egg water and other stimuli," *Biol. Bull.*, 103: 54–66.

————, 1954. "Studies on the acrosome. II. Acrosome reaction in starfish spermatozoa. III. Effect of calcium deficiency," *Biol. Bull.*, 107: 203–218.

————, 1960. "Studies on the acrosome. VI. Fine structure of the starfish acrosome," *Exptl. Cell Res.*, 19: 13–28.

————, 1962. "The vitelline coat of the *Mytilus* egg. 1. Normal structure and effect of acrosomal lysin," *Biol. Bull.*, 124: 531–541.

————, Ohori, Y., and Kushida, H., 1964. "Studies on the acrosome. VII. Formation of the acrosomal process in sea urchin spermatozoa," *J. Ultrastr. Res.*, 11: 508–524.

————, and WADA, S. K., 1955. "Studies on the acrosome. IV. The acrosome reaction in some bivalve spermatozoa," *Biol. Bull.*, 109: 40–55.

DANIELLI, J. F., 1942. "The cell surface and cell physiology," pp. 68–98 in G. Bourne, ed., *Cytology and Cell Physiology*, Oxford: Clarendon Press.

DELAGE, Y., 1901. "Etudes expérimentales chez les Echinodermes." *Arch. Zool. Exp. et Gén.*, Sér. 3, 9: 285–326.

DENNY, P. C., and TYLER, A., 1964. "Activation of protein biosynthesis in non-nucleate fragments of sea urchin eggs," *Biochim. Biophys. Res. Comm.*, 14: 245–249.

DETTLAFF, T. A., 1962. "Cortical changes in acipenserid eggs during fertilization and artificial activation," *J. Embryol. Exp. Morphol.*, 10: 1-26.

————, and GINSBURG, A. S., 1963. "Acrosome reaction in sturgeons and the role of Ca-ions in sperm-egg association," *Doklady Akad. Nauk SSSR*, **153**: 1461–1464.

DICKMANN, Z., 1963. "Chemotaxis of rabbit spermatozoa," *J. Exper. Biol.*, **40**: 1–6.

DIRKSEN, E. R., 1961. "The presence of centrioles in artificially activated sea urchin eggs," *J. Bioph. Bioch. Cytol.*, **11**: 244–247.

EAST, E. M., 1929. "Self-sterility," *Bibliogr. Genetica*, **5**: 331.

ECKER, R. E., and BROOKBANK, J. W., 1963. "A ribosome fraction from sand dollar *(Mellita quinquiesperforata)* ova," *Biochim. Biophys. Acta*, **72**: 490–493.

ENDO, Y., 1952. "The role of the cortical granules in the formation of the fertilization membrane in eggs from Japanese sea urchins. I," *Exptl. Cell Res.*, **3**: 406–418.

————, 1961a. "Changes in the cortical layer of sea urchin eggs at fertilization as studied with the electron microscope. I. *Clypeaster japonicus*," *Exptl. Cell Res.*, **25**: 383–397.

————, 1961b. "The role of the cortical granules in the formation of the fertilization membrane in the eggs of sea urchins. II," *Exptl. Cell Res.*, **25**: 518–528.

FAN, D. P., HIGA, A., and LEVINTHAL, C., 1964. "Messenger RNA decay and protection," *J. Mol. Biol.*, **8**: 223–230.

FANKHAUSER, G., 1925. "Analyse der physiologischen Polyspermie des Triton-Eies auf Grund von Schnürungsexperimenten," *Arch. Entw. Mech.*, **105**: 501–580.

————, 1932. "Cytological studies on egg fragments of the Salamander Triton. 2. The history of the supernumerary sperm nuclei in normal fertilization and cleavage of fragments containing the egg nucleus," *J. Exper. Zool.*, **62**: 185–235.

————, 1948. "The organization of the amphibian egg during fertilization and cleavage." *Ann. N. Y. Acad. Sci.*, **49**: 684–707.

FAURÉ-FREMIET, E., 1922. "Echanges respiratoires des oeufs de *Sabellaria alveolata* L. au cours de la segmentation et de la cytolyse," *C. R. Soc. Biol.*, **86**: 20–23.

FEKETE, E., and DURAN REYNALS, F., 1942. "Hyaluronidase in the fertilization of mammalian ova," *Proc. Soc. Exp. Biol. Med.*, **52**: 119–121.

FICQ, A., 1955. "Etude autoradiographique du métabolisme de l'oocyte d'*Asterias rubens* au cours de la croissance," *Arch. Biol.*, **66**: 509–524.

————, 1961. "Localization of different types of ribonucleic acids (RNA's) in amphibian oocytes," *Exptl. Cell Res.*, **23**: 427–429.

FLEMMING, W., 1881. "Beiträge zur Kenntnis der Zelle und ihrer Lebenserscheinungen. 3," *Arch. mikr. Anat.*, **20**: 1–86.

FOL, H., 1878–1879. "Recherches sur la fécondation et le commencement de l'hénogénie chez divers animaux," *Mem. Soc. Phys. et Hist. Nat. Genève*, **26**: 89–250.

FOLKES, B. F., GRANT, R. A., and JONES, J. K. N., 1950. "Frog spawn mucin," *J. Chem. Soc.*, **440**: 2136–2140.

FÖRSTER, H., WIESE, L., and BRAUNITZER, G., 1956. "Ueber das agglutinierend wirkende Gynogamon von *Chlamydomonas eugametos*," *Ztsch. f. Naturforsch.* 11b: 315–317.

FRÉDÉRIC, J., 1958. "Recherches cytologiques sur le chondriome normal ou soumis à l'expérimentation dans des cellules vivantes cultivées *in vitro*," *Arch. Biol.,* 69: 167–349.

FRIEDMANN, J., 1962. "Cell membrane fusion and the fertilization mechanism in plants and animals," *Science,* 136: 711–712.

FUJII, T., and OHNISHI, T., 1963. "Inhibition of acid production at fertilization by nicotinamide and other inhibitors of diphosphopyridine nucleotidase (DPNase) in the sea urchin," *J. Fac. Sci. Univ. Tokyo,* Sect. IV, 9: 333.

GHIRETTI, F., and D'AMELIO, V., 1956. "The metabolism of pentose phosphate in sea urchin sperm and eggs," *Exptl. Cell Res.,* 10: 734–737.

GIACOSA, P., 1882. "Etudes sur la composition chimique de l'oeuf et de ses enveloppes chez la grenouille commune. 1. Sur l'enveloppe muqueuse de l'oeuf," *Z. physiol. Chem.,* 7: 40–56.

GIARDINA, A., 1902a. "Note sul meccanismo della fecondazione e della divisione cellulare, studiato principalmente sulle uova di echini," *Anat. Anz.,* 21: 561–581.

———, 1902b. "Note sul meccanismo della fecondazione e della divisione cellulare, studiato principalmente in uova di echini," *Anat. Anz.,* 22: 40–58.

GIARDINA, G., and MONROY, A., 1955. "Changes in the proteins of the sea urchin egg at fertilization," *Exptl. Cell Res.,* 8: 466–473.

GIERER, A., 1963. "Function of aggregated retyculocyte ribosomes in protein synthesis," *J. Mol. Biol.,* 6: 148–157.

GILBERT, W., 1963. "Polypeptide synthesis in *Escherichia coli*. 1. Ribosomes and the active complex," *J. Mol. Biol.,* 6: 374–388.

GINSBURG, A. S., 1961. "The block to polyspermy in sturgeon and trout with special reference to the role of cortical granules (alveoli) ," *J. Embryol. Exp. Morphol.,* 9: 173–190.

———, 1963a. "Sperm-egg association and its relationship to the activation of the egg in salmonid fishes," *J. Embryol. Exp. Morphol.,* 11: 13–33.

———, 1963b. "On the mechanism of egg protection against polyspermy in echinoderm," *Doklady Akad. Nauk SSSR,* 152: 501–504.

GIUDICE, G., 1960. "Incorporation of labelled amino acids in the proteins of the mitochondria isolated from unfertilized eggs and developmental stages of *Paracentrotus lividus*," *Exptl. Cell Res.,* 21: 222–225.

———, VITTORELLI, M. L., and MONROY, A., 1962. "Investigations on the protein metabolism during the early development of the sea urchin," *Acta Embryol. Morphol. Exper.,* 5: 113–122.

GLASS, B., and PLAINE, H. L., 1950. "The immediate dependence of the action of a specific gene in *Drosophila melanogaster* upon fertilization," *Proc. Natl. Acad. Sci.,* 36: 627–634.

GOODRICH, H. B., 1920. "Rapidity of activation in the fertilization of *Nereis*," *Biol. Bull.,* 38: 196–201.

GRAY, J., 1928. "The effect of egg secretion on the activity of spermatozoa," *J. Exp. Biol.*, 5: 362–365.

GROSS, P. R., and COUSINEAU, G. H., 1963. "Effects of Actinomycin D on macromolecule synthesis and early development in sea urchin eggs," *Biochem. Biophys. Res. Comm.*, 10: 321–326.

——, ——, 1964. "Macromolecule synthesis and the influence of actinomycin on early development," *Exptl. Cell Res.*, 33: 368–395.

——, MALKIN, L. I., and MOYER, W. A., 1964. "Template for the first proteins of embryonic development," *Proc. Natl. Acad. Sci.*, 51: 407–414.

GRUNDFEST, H., KAO, C. Y., MONROY, A., and TYLER, A., 1955. "Existence of a resting potential in the egg of the starfish *Asterias forbesii*," *Biol. Bull.*, 109: 346.

HADEK, R., 1963a. "Submicroscopic changes in the penetrating spermatozoon of the rabbit," *J. Ultrastr. Res.*, 8: 161–169.

——, 1963b. "Submicroscopic study of the cortical granules in the rabbit ovum," *J. Ultrastr. Res.*, 8: 170–175.

——, 1963c. "Submicroscopic study on the sperm-induced cortical reaction in the rabbit ovum," *J. Ultrastr. Res.*, 9: 99–109.

HAGSTRÖM, B., and HAGSTRÖM, B., 1954. "Re-fertilization of the sea urchin egg," *Exptl. Cell Res.*, 6: 491–496.

HAMANO, S., 1957. "Physico-chemical studies on the activation and fertilization of fish egg," *Mem. Fac. Fish. Hokkaido Univ.*, 5: 91–143.

HARDING, C. V., HARDING, D., and PERLMANN, P., 1954. "Antigens in sea urchin hybrid embryos," *Exptl. Cell Res.*, 6: 202–210.

HARTMANN, M., and SCHARTAU, O., 1939. "Untersuchungen über die Befruchtungsstoffe der Seeigel. 1. Mitt.," *Biol. Zbl.*, 59: 571–587.

——, ——, KUHN, R., and WALLENFELS, K., 1939. "Ueber die Sexualstoffe der Seeigel," *Naturwiss.*, 27: 433.

——, ——, and WALLENFELS, K., 1940. "Untersuchungen über die Befruchtungsstoffe der Seeigel. 2. Mitt.," *Biol. Zbl.*, 60: 398–423.

HARVEY, E. B., 1936. "Parthenogenetic merogony or cleavage without nuclei in *Arbacia punctulata*," *Biol. Bull.*, 71: 101–121.

HATHAWAY, R. R., 1959. "The effect of sperm on ^{35}S-labelled *Arbacia* fertilizin," *Biol. Bull.*, 117: 395.

——, 1963. "Activation of respiration in sea urchin spermatozoa by egg water," *Biol. Bull.*, 125: 486–498.

——, and METZ, CH. B., 1961. "Interaction between *Arbacia* sperm and S[35]-labelled fertilizin," *Biol. Bull.*, 120: 360–369.

HAUSCHKA, S. D., 1963. "Purification and characterization of *Mytilus* egg membrane lysin from sperm," *Biol. Bull.*, 125: 363.

HAYASHI, T., 1946. "Dilution medium and survival of the spermatozoa of *Arbacia punctulata*. II. Effect of the medium on respiration," *Biol. Bull.*, 90: 177–187.

HILL, D. K., and KEYNES, R. D., 1949. "Opacity changes in stimulated nerve," *J. Physiol.*, 108: 278–281.

HIRAMOTO, Y., 1959a. "Electric properties of echinoderm eggs," *Embryologia*, 4: 219–235.

——, 1959b. "Changes in electric properties upon fertilization in the sea urchin egg," *Exptl. Cell Res.*, 16: 421–424.

——, 1962a. "Microinjection of the live spermatozoa into sea urchin eggs," *Exptl. Cell Res.*, 27: 416–426.

——, 1962b. "An analysis of the mechanism of fertilization by means of enucleation of sea urchin eggs," *Exptl. Cell Res.*, 28: 323–334.

HIYAMA, N., 1949a. "Biochemical studies on carbohydrates. On the jelly of toad and frog eggs. I," *Tohoku J. Exp. Med.*, 50: 373–378.

——, 1949b. "Biochemical studies on carbohydrates. Hexosamine in the toad mucin," *Tohoku J. Exp. Med.*, 50: 379–383.

——, 1949c. "Biochemical studies on carbohydrates. Hexosamine in the frog mucin," *Tohoku J. Exp. Med.*, 50: 385–387.

HOBERMANN, H. D., METZ, CH. B., and GRAFF, J., 1952. "Uptake of deuterium into proteins of fertilized and unfertilized *Arbacia* eggs suspended in heavy water," *J. Gen. Phys.*, 35: 639–643.

HODGKIN, A. L., 1951. "The ionic basis of electrical activity in nerve and muscle," *Biol. Rev.*, 26: 339–409.

HOFF-JØRGENSEN, E., 1954. "Deoxyribonucleic acid in some gametes and embryos," *Proc. 7th Symp. Colston Res. Soc. Univ. Bristol*, p. 79.

——, and ZEUTHEN, E., 1952. "Evidence of cytoplasmic deoxyribosides in the frog's egg," *Nature*, 169: 245–246.

HOLLAND, J. J., and McLAREN, L. C., 1959. "The mammalian cell-virus relationship. II. Adsorption, reception and eclipse of poliovirus by HeLa cells," *J. Exp. Med.*, 109: 487–504.

——, ——, and SYVERTON, J. T., 1959a. "The mammalian cell-virus relationship. III. Poliovirus production by non-primate cells exposed to poliovirus RNA," *Proc. Soc. Exp. Biol. Med.*, 100: 843–845.

——, ——, ——, 1959b. "The mammalian cell-virus relationship. IV. Infection of naturally insusceptible cells with enterovirus nucleic acid," *J. Exp. Med.*, 110: 65–80.

HOLTER, H., and ZEUTHEN, E., 1944. "The respiration of the egg and embryos of the ascidian, *Ciona intestinalis* L.," *C. R. Trav. Lab. Carlsberg*, Sér. Chim., 25: 33–65.

HULTIN, T., 1950. "The protein metabolism of sea urchin eggs during early development studied by means of N^{15}-labelled ammonia," *Exptl. Cell Res.*, 1: 599–602.

——, 1952. "Incorporation of N^{15}-labelled glycine and alanine into the proteins of developing sea urchin eggs," *Exptl. Cell Res.*, 3: 494–496.

——, 1953a. "The amino acids metabolism of sea urchin embryos studied by means of N^{15}-labelled ammonium chloride and alanine," *Ark. f. kemi*, 5: 543–552.

——, 1953b. "Incorporation of N^{15}-dl-alanine into protein fractions of sea urchin embryos," *Ark. f. kemi*, 5: 559–564.

———, 1961. "Activation of ribosomes in sea urchin eggs in response to fertilization," *Exptl. Cell Res.*, 25: 405–417.

———, and BERGSTRAND, Å., 1960. Incorporation of C^{14}-L-leucine into protein by cell-free system from sea urchin embryos at different stages of development," *Dev. Biol.*, 2: 61–75.

———, and WESSEL, G., 1952. "Incorporation of C^{14}-labeled carbon dioxide into the proteins of developing sea urchin eggs," *Exptl. Cell Res.*, 3: 613–616.

HUMPHREYS, W. J., 1962. "Electron microscope studies on eggs of *Mytilus edulis*," *J. Ultrastr. Res.*, 7: 467–487.

IIDA, T. T., 1949. "Changes of electric capacitance following artificial activation in sea urchin eggs," *Zool. Mag.*, 58: 122–125.

IMMERS, J., 1961. "The occurrence of sulphated mucopolysaccharide in the perivitelline liquid of *Echinus esculentus*," *Ark. Zool.*, 13, 299–306.

———, and RUNNSTRÖM, J., 1960. "Release of respiratory control by 2,4-dinitrophenol in different stages of sea urchin development," *Dev. Biol.*, 2: 90–104.

INFANTELLINA, F., and LA GRUTTA, G., 1948. "Contenuto in glutatione nelle uova di *Paracentrotus lividus* e sue variazioni nelle varie fasi dello sviluppo," *Arch. Sc. Biol.*, 32: 85–106.

ISHIDA, J., and NAKANO, E., 1947. "Fertilization of activated sea urchin eggs deprived of fertilization membrane," *Dobutsugaku zasshi*, 57: 117.

———, ———, 1950. "Fertilization of activated sea urchin eggs deprived of fertilization membrane by washing with Ca-Mg-free media," *Ann. Zool. Jap.*, 23: 43–48.

ISHIHARA, K., 1957. "Release and activation of aldolase at fertilization in sea urchin egg," *J. Fac. Sci. Univ. Tokyo*, Sect. IV, 8: 71–93.

———, 1958a. "Effect of butyric acid on aldolase complex in sea urchin eggs," *Sci. Rep. Saitama Univ.*, B, 3: 11–20.

———, 1958b. "Enhanced respiration of sea urchin eggs induced by mechanical stimulation," *"Sci. Rep. Saitama Univ.*, B, 3: 21–32.

———, 1963. "Isolation of aldolase complex in sea urchin eggs," *Sci. Rep. Saitama Univ.*, B, 6: 173–179.

ISHIKAWA, M., 1954. "Relation between the breakdown of the cortical granules and permeability to water in the sea urchin egg," *Embryologia*, 2: 57–62.

ISONO, N., 1963. "Carbohydrate metabolism in sea urchin eggs. 4. Intracellular localization of enzymes of pentose phosphate cycle in unfertilized and fertilized eggs," *J. Fac. Sci. Univ. Toyko*, Sect. 4, 10: 37–53.

———, ISUSAKA, A., and NAKANO, E., 1963. "Studies on glucose-6-phosphate dehydrogenase in sea urchin eggs. 1," *J. Fac. Sci. Univ. Tokyo*, Sect. 4, 10: 55–66.

ITO, S., 1960. "The osmotic property of the unfertilized egg of fresh water fish, *Oryzias latipes*," *Kumamoto J. of Sci.*, Ser. B, 5: 61–72.

———, 1962. "Resting potential and activation potential of the *Oryzias* egg. 2. Change of membrane potential and resistance during fertilization," *Embryologia*, 7: 47–55.

132 · REFERENCES

————, and MAENO, T., 1960. "Resting potential and activation potential of the *Oryzias* egg. 1. Response to electrical stimulation," *Kumamoto J. of Sci.*, Ser. B, 5: 100–107.

JUST, E. E., 1919. "The fertilization reaction in *Echinarachnius parma*. 1. Cortical response of the egg to insemination," *Biol. Bull.*, 36: 1–10.

KACSER, H., 1955. "The cortical changes on fertilization of the sea urchin egg," *J. Exp. Biol.*, 32: 451–467.

KAO, C. Y., 1955. "Changing electrical constants of the *Fundulus* egg surface," *Biol. Bull.*, 109: 361.

KELTCH, A. K., KRAHL, M. E., and CLOWES, G. H. A., 1956. "Alteration by dinitrocresol of pathways for glucose oxidation in eggs of *Arbacia punctulata*," *J. Gen. Physiol.*, 40: 27–35.

KIHO, Y., and RICH, A., 1964. "Induced enzyme formed on bacterial polyribosomes," *Proc. Natl. Acad. Sci.*, 51: 111–118.

KLOTZ, I. M., 1958. "Protein hydration and behaviour," *Science*, 128: 815–822.

KÖHLER, K., and METZ, CH. B., 1960. "Antigens of the sea urchin sperm surface," *Biol. Bull.*, 118: 96–110.

KONECNY, M., 1959. "Etude histochimique de la zone pellucide des ovules de chatte," *C. R. Soc. Biol. Paris*, 153: 893–894.

KRAHL, M. E., 1956. "Oxidative pathway for glucose in eggs of the sea urchin," *Biochim. Biophys. Acta*, 20: 27–32.

KRANE, S. M., and CRANE, R. K., 1960. "Changes in levels of triphosphopyridine nucleotide in marine eggs subsequent to fertilization," *Biochim. Biophys. Acta*, 43: 369–373.

KRAUSS, M., 1950a. "On the question of hyaluronidase in sea urchin spermatozoa," *Science*, 112: 759.

————, 1950b. "Lytic agents of the sperm of some marine animals. 1. The egg membrane lysin from sperm of the giant keyhole limpet, *Megathura crenulata*," *J. Exp. Zool.*, 114: 239–278.

————, 1950c. "Lytic agents of the sperm of some marine animals. 2. Extraction of a hetero-egg membrane lysin from sea urchin sperm," *J. Exp. Zool.*, 114: 279–292.

KROEGER, H., 1963. "Chemical nature of the system controlling gene activities in insect cells," *Nature*, 200: 1234–1235.

KROH, M., and LINSKENS, H. F., 1963a. "Biochemie der Befruchtungs-Inkompatibilität," *Umschau*, 9: 266–269.

————, ————, 1963b. "Biochemie der Befruchtungs-Inkompatibilität. Die Ursache der Unfruchtbarkeit von Blütenpflanzen bei Selbstbestäubung. II," *Umschau*, 10: 313–314.

KUHN, R., and WALLENFELS, K., 1940. "Echinochrome als prosthetische Gruppen hochmolekulären Symplexe in den Eiern von *Arbacia pustulosa*," *Berichte deutsch. Chem. Ges.*, 73: 458–464.

KUSA, M., 1951. quoted by Ito, 1960.

————, 1956. "Studies on cortical alveoli in some teleostean eggs," *Embryologia*, 3: 105–129.

LARDY, H. A., and WELLMAN, H., 1952. "Oxydative phosphorylations: role of inorganic phosphate and acceptor systems in control of metabolic rates," *J. Biol. Chem.*, **195**: 215–224.

LASER, H., and ROTHSCHILD, LORD, 1939. "The metabolism of the eggs of *Psammechinus miliaris* during the fertilization reaction," *Proc. Roy. Soc. London*, **B 126**: 539–557.

LEHNINGER, A. L., 1962. "Water uptake and extrusion by mitochondria in relation to oxidative phosphorylation," *Physiol. Rev.*, **42**: 467–517.

LENTINI, R., 1961. "The oxygen uptake of *Ciona intestinalis* eggs during development in normal and in experimental conditions," *Acta Embryol. Morphol. Exper.*, **4**: 209–218.

LILLIE, F. R., 1906. "Observations and experiments confirming the elementary phenomena of embryonic development in *Chaetopterus*," *J. Exper. Zool.*, **3**: 153–268.

——, 1911. "Studies of fertilization of *Nereis*. 1. The cortical changes in the egg. 2. Partial fertilization," *J. Morphol.*, **22**: 695–730.

——, 1912. "Studies of fertilization in *Nereis*. 3. The morphology of normal fertilization of *Nereis*. 4. The fertilizing power of portions of the spermatozoon," *J. Exp. Zool.*, **12**: 413–478.

——, 1913. "Studies of fertilization. 5. The behaviour of the spermatozoa of *Nereis* and *Arbacia* with special reference to egg-extractives," *J. Exp. Zool.*, **14**: 515–574.

——, 1914. "Studies of fertilization. 6. The mechanism of fertilization in *Arbacia*," *J. Exp. Zool.*, **16**: 523–590.

LILLIE, R. S., 1916. "Increase of permeability of water following normal and artificial activation in the sea urchin eggs," *Amer. J. Physiol.*, **40**: 249–266.

LINDAHL, P. E., 1938. "Ueber die Atmungshemmende und Atmungserhöhende Wirkung des Kohlenoxyds," *Naturwiss.*, **26**: 709–710.

——, and HOLTER, H., 1941. "Ueber die Atmung der Ovozyten erster Ordnung von *Paracentrotus lividus* und ihre Veränderung während der Reifung," *C. R. Tr. Lab. Carlsberg, Sér. Chim.*, **24**: 49–57.

LINDBERG, O., 1943. "Studien ueber das Problem des Kohlehydratabbaus und der Säurebildung bei der Befruchtung des Seeigeleies," *Ark. f. Kemi, Min. o. Geol.*, **16 A**: Nr. 15.

——, 1945. "On the metabolism of glycogen in the fertilization of the sea urchin egg," *Ark. f. Kemi, Min. o. Geol.*, **20 B**: Nr. 1.

——, 1950. "On surface reactions in the sea urchin egg," *Exptl. Cell Res.*, **1**: 105–114.

——, and ERNSTER, L., 1948. "On carbohydrate metabolism in homogenized sea urchin eggs," *Biochem. Biophys. Acta*, **2**: 471–477.

LINDERSTRÖM-LANG, K. U., 1952. "Proteins and enzymes," pp. 115. *Lane Medical Lectures*, Palo Alto, Calif.: Stanford University Publ., Medical Sciences, Vol. VI.

LINSKENS, H. F., 1953. "Physiologische und chemische Unterschiede zwischen selbst- und fremdbestäubten Petunien-Griffeln," *Naturwiss.*, **40**: 28–29.

———, 1955. "Physiologische Untersuchungen der Pollenschlauch Hemmung selbst-steriler Petunien," *Z. Bot.*, **43**: 1–44.

———, 1965. "Biochesmistry of incompatibility," *Genetics today, Proc. XI Internatl. Congress of Genetics*, Vol. II, New York: Pergamon Press (in press).

LITCHFIELD, J. B., and WHITELEY, A. H., 1959. "Studies on the mechanism of phosphate accumulation by sea urchin embryos," *Biol. Bull.*, **117**: 133–149.

LUNDBLAD, G., 1949. "Proteolytic activity in eggs and sperms from sea urchins," *Nature*, **163**: 643.

———, 1950. "Proteolytic activity in sea urchin gametes," *Exptl. Cell Res.*, **1**: 264–271.

———, 1952. "Proteolytic activity in sea urchin gametes. 2. Activity of extracts and homogenates of the egg subjected to different treatments," *Ark. f. Kemi*, **4**: 537–565.

———, 1954a. "Proteolytic activity in sea urchin gametes. 4. Further investigations of the proteolytic enzymes of the egg," *Ark. f. Kemi*, **7**: 127–157.

———, 1954b. "Proteolytic activity in sea urchin gametes. 6. A study of a proteolytic enzyme in extracts of spermatozoa," *Ark. f. Kemi*, **7**: 169–180.

———, and LUNDBLAD, I., 1953. "Proteolytic activity in sea urchin gametes. 3. A study of the proteolytic enzymes of the egg," *Ark. f. Kemi*, **6**: 387–415.

MAENO, T., 1959. "Electrical characteristics and activation potential of *Bufo* eggs," *J. Gen. Physiol.*, **43**: 139–157.

———, MORITA, H., and KUWABARA, M., 1956. "Potential measurements on the eggs of Japanese killi-fish, *Oryzias latipes*," *Mem. Fac. Sci Kyushu Univ.*, Ser. E, **2**: 87–94.

MAGGIO, R., 1957. "Mitochondrial and cytoplasmic protease activity in sea urchin eggs," *J. Cell. Comp. Physiol.*, **50**: 135–144.

———, 1959. "Cytochrome oxidase activity in the mitochondria of unfertilized and fertilized sea urchin eggs," *Exptl. Cell Res.*, **16**: 272–278.

———, AIELLO, F., and MONROY, A., 1960. "Inhibitor of cytochrome oxidase of unfertilized sea urchin eggs," *Nature*, **188**: 1195–1196.

———, and CATALANO, C., 1963. "Activation of amino acids during sea urchin development," *Arch. Bioch. Bioph.*, **103**: 164–167.

———, and GHIRETTI-MAGALDI, A., 1958. "The cytochrome system in mitochondria of unfertilized sea urchin eggs," *Exptl. Cell Res.*, **15**: 95–102.

———, and MONROY, A., 1955. "Some experiments pertaining to the chemical mechanisms of the cortical reaction in fertilization of sea urchin eggs," *Exptl. Cell Res.*, **8**: 240–244.

———, ———, 1959. "An inhibitor of cytochrome oxidase activity in the sea urchin egg," *Nature*, **184**: 68–69.

———, VITTORELLI, M. L., RINALDI, A. M., and MONROY, A., 1964. "In vitro incorporation of amino acids into protein stimulated by RNA from unfertilized sea urchin eggs," *Bioch. Bioph. Res. Comm.*, **15**: 436–441.

MARCUS, L., BRETTHAUER, R. K., BOCK, R. M., and HALVORSON, H. O., 1963. "The effect of poly-U size on the incorporation of phenylalanine in the cell-free yeast system," *Proc. Natl. Acad. Sci.*, **50**: 782–789.

MARKS, P. A., BURKA, E. R., and SCHLESSINGER, D., 1962. "Protein synthesis in erythroid cells. 1. Reticulocyte ribosomes active in stimulating amino acid incorporation," *Proc. Natl. Acad. Sci.*, 48: 2163–2171.

———, ———, RIFKIND, R., and DANON, D., 1963. "Polyribosomes active in reticulocyte protein synthesis," *Cold Spring Harbor Symp. Quant. Biol.*, 28: 223–226.

MAZIA, D., 1937. "The release of calcium in *Arbacia* eggs on fertilization," *J. Cell. Comp. Physiol.*, 10: 291–304.

———, 1959. "The role of thiol groups in the structure and function of the mitotic apparatus," pp. 367–389 in R. Benesch *et al.*, eds., *Sulfur in Proteins*, New York: Academic Press.

McCARTHY, B. J., BRITTEN, R. J., and ROBERTS, R. B., 1962. "The synthesis of ribosomes in *E. coli*. 3. Synthesis of ribosomal RNA," *Biophys. J.*, 2: 57–82.

McCULLOCH, D., 1952. "Note on the origin of the cortical granules in *Arbacia punctulata* eggs," *Exptl. Cell Res.*, 3: 605–607.

McLAREN, L. C., HOLLAND, J. J., and SYVERTON, J. T., 1959. "The mammalian cell-virus relationship. 1. Attachment of poliovirus to cultivated cells of primate and non-primate origin," *J. Exp. Med.*, 109: 475–485.

McLEAN, D., and ROWLANDS, L. W., 1942. "Role of hyaluronidase in fertilization," *Nature*, 150: 627–628.

MEDEM, VON, GRAF F., 1942. "Beiträge zur Frage der Befruchtungsstoffe bei marinen Mollusken," *Biol. Zbl.*, 62: 431–446.

———, 1945. "Untersuchungen über die Ei- und Spermwirkstoffe bei marinen Mollusken," *Zool. Jahrb., Abt. Allg. Zool. u. Physiol.*, 61: 5–44.

MEHL, J. W., and SWANN, M. M., 1961. "Acid and base production at fertilization in the sea urchin," *Exptl. Cell Res.*, 22: 233–245.

MERCER, E. H., and WOLPERT, L., 1962. "An electron microscope study of the cortex of the sea urchin (*Psammechinus miliaris*) egg," *Exptl. Cell Res.*, 27: 1–13.

MESSINA, L., 1954. "The metachromatic properties of the jelly coat of the sea urchin egg as a means for the study of the jelly-coat-sperm interaction," *Pubbl. Staz. Zool. Napoli*, 25: 454–458.

———, and MONROY, A., 1956. "Evidence for the inhomogeneity of the jelly coat of the sea urchin egg," *Pubbl. Staz. Zool. Napoli*, 28: 266–268.

METZ, CH. B., 1945. "The agglutination of starfish sperm by fertilizin," *Biol. Bull.*, 89: 84–94.

———, 1962. "Immunochemical studies on fertilization mechanisms," *Proc. Conference on Immuno-Reproduction*, The Population Council, New York, pp. 107–115.

METZ, CH. B., SCHUEL, H., and BISCHOFF, E. R., 1964. "Inhibition of the fertilizing capacity of sea-urchin sperm by papain-digested, non-agglutinating antibody," *J. Exper. Zool.* 155: 261–272.

MEVES, F., 1912. "Verfolgung des sogenannten Mittelstückes des Echinidienspermiums in befruchteten Ei bis zum Ende der ersten Furchungsteilung," *Arch. f. mikr. Anat.*, 80: 81–123.

———, 1914. "Verfolgung des Mittelstückes des Echinidienspermiums durch die ersten Zellgenerationen des befruchteten Eies," *Arch. f. mikr. Anat.*, 85: 279–302.

MINGANTI, A., 1948. "Interspecific fertilization in ascidians," *Nature*, **161**: 643–644.

———, 1950. "Esperimenti di ibridazione interspecifica nelle Ascidie," *Pubbl. Staz. Zool. Napoli*, **22**: 293–307.

———, 1951. "Esperienze sulla fertilizina nelle Ascidie," *Pubbl. Staz. Zool. Napoli*, **23**: 1–8.

———, 1954. "Sui glicidi della gelatina ovulare degli Anfibi," *Ric. Scientifica*, **24**: 1658–1661.

———, 1955. "Chemical investigations on amphibian egg jellies," *Exptl. Cell Res.*, Suppl. **3**: 248–251.

———, 1957. "Experiments on the respiration of *Phallusia* eggs and embryos (ascidians) ," *Acta Embryol. Morphol. Exper.*, **1**: 150–163.

———, and AZZOLINA, G., 1956. "Attività proteolitica dell'enzima della schiusa di *Bufo* e *Discoglossus*," *Ric. Scientifica*, **25**: 2103–2108.

———, and D'ANNA, T., 1957. "Ricerche sulla mucina ovulare di *Triton cristatus*," *Ric. Scientifica*, **27**: 3052–3054.

———, ———, 1958. "Sulla composizione della mucina ovulare di *Discoglossus pictus*," *Ric. Scientifica*, **28**, 2090–2094 .

———, and VASSEUR, E., 1959. "An analysis of the jelly substance of *Paracentrotus* eggs," *Acta Embryol. Morphol. Exper.*, **2**: 195–203.

MIRSKY, A. E., 1936. "Protein coagulation as a result of fertilization," *Science*, **84**: 333–334.

MITCHISON, J. M., 1952. "Cell membranes and cell division," *Symp. Soc. Exptl. Biol.*, **6**: 105–127.

MONNÉ, L., and HÅRDE, S., 1951. "On the cortical granules of the sea urchin egg," *Ark. f. Zool.*, ser. 2, **1**: 487–498.

———, ———, 1952. "Changes in the protoplasmic properties occurring upon stimulation and inhibition of the cellular activities," *Ark. f. Zool.*, **3**: 289–318.

MONOD, J., CHANGEUX, J.-P., and JACOB, F., 1963. "Allosteryc proteins and cellular control systems," *J. Mol. Biol.*, **6**: 306–329.

MONROY, A., 1945. "Di alcuni fenomeni corticali che accompagnano la fecondazione e le prime divisioni dell'uovo di riccio di mare," *Experientia*, **1**: 335–336.

———, 1947. "Further observations on the fine structure of the cortical layer of unfertilized and fertilized sea urchin eggs," *J. Cell. Comp. Physiol.*, **30**: 105–110.

———, 1948a. "Cortical changes accompanying maturation in sea urchin egg," *Experientia*, **4**: 353–358.

———, 1948b. "A preliminary approach to the physiology of fertilization in *Pomatoceros triqueter L.*," *Ark. f. Zool.*, **40 A**: No. 21.

———, 1949. "On the formation of the fertilization membrane in the sea urchin, *Psammechinus micr.*," *Proc. VI Internatl. Congress on Exptl. Cytol., Exptl. Cell Res.*, Suppl. I: 525–528.

———, 1950. "A preliminary electrophoretic analysis of proteins and protein fractions in sea urchin eggs and their changes on fertilization," *Exptl. Cell Res.*, **1**: 92–104.

———, 1953. "A model for the cortical reaction of fertilization in the sea urchin egg," *Experientia*, 9: 424.

———, 1954. "Observations on the fertilization reaction in the eggs of some polychaetes and an ascidian, with special reference to the cortical changes," *Pubbl. Staz. Zool. Napoli*, 25: 188–197.

———, 1956. "Some experiments concerning the chemical mechanisms of the activation of the sea urchin egg," *Exptl. Cell Res.*, 10: 320–323.

———, 1957a. "Swelling properties of the mitochondria of unfertilized and newly fertilized sea urchin eggs," *Experientia*, 13: 398.

———, 1957b. "Studies of proteins of sea urchin egg and of their changes following fertilization," pp. 169–174 in A. Tyler, R. C. von Borstel, and Ch. B. Metz, eds. *The Beginning of Embryonic Development*, Washington, D.C.: American Assoc. for the Advancement of Science.

———, 1960. "Incorporation of S^{35}-methionine in the microsomes and soluble proteins during the early development of the sea urchin egg," *Experientia*, 16: 114–117.

———, and MONROY ODDO, A., 1946. "Ricerche sulla fisiologia della fecondazione. Nota I. Natura dello strato corticale dell'uovo vergine di riccio di mare," *Pubbl. Staz. Zool. Napoli*, 20: 46–60.

———, ———, 1951. "Solubility changes of proteins in sea urchin eggs upon fertilization," *J. Gen. Physiol.*, 35: 245–253.

———, and MONTALENTI, G., 1947. "Variations of the submicroscopic structure of the cortical layer of fertilized and parthenogenetic sea urchin eggs," *Biol. Bull.*, 92: 151–161.

———, and RUFFO, A., 1947. "Hyaluronidase in sea urchin sperm," *Nature*, 159: 603.

———, and RUNNSTRÖM, J., 1948. "Some experiments pertaining to the chemical changes occurring at the formation of the fertilization membrane of sea urchin egg," *Ark. f. Zool.*, 40 A: No. 18.

———, and TOLIS, H., 1964. "Uptake of radioactive glucose and amino acids and their utilization for incorporation into proteins during maturation and fertilization of the eggs of *Asterias forbesii* and *Spisula solidissima*," *Biol. Bull.*, 126: 456–466.

———, and TOSI, L., 1952. "A note on the jelly-coat-sperm interaction in sea urchin," *Experientia*, 8: 393–396.

———, TOSI, L., GIARDINA, G., and MAGGIO, R., 1954. "Further investigations on the interactions between sperm and jelly coat in the fertilization of the sea urchin egg," *Biol. Bull.*, 106: 169–177.

———, and TYLER, A., 1963. "Formation of active ribosomal aggregates (polysomes) upon fertilization and development of sea urchin eggs," *Arch. Bioch. Bioph.*, 103: 431–435.

———, and VITTORELLI, M. L., 1960. "On a glycoprotein of the sea urchin eggs and its changes following fertilization," *Experientia*, 16: 56–59.

———, ———, 1962. "Utilization of ^{14}C-glucose for amino acids and protein synthesis by the sea urchin embryo," *J. Cell. Comp. Physiol.*, 60: 285–288.

MONROY ODDO, A., 1946. "Variations in Ca and Mg contents in *Arbacia* eggs as a result of fertilization," *Experientia*, 2: 371–372.

———, and ESPOSITO, M., 1951. "Changes in the potassium content of sea urchin eggs on fertilization," *J. Gen. Physiol.*, **34:** 285–293.

MONTALENTI, G., 1949. "Ulteriori osservazioni sui gamoni della Lampreda (*Lampetra fluviatilis*)," *Pubbl. Staz. Zool. Napoli*, **22:** 6–9.

———, and SCHARTAU, O., 1942. "Ricerche sulle reazioni della fecondazione e sulla presenza di gamoni nella Lampreda (*Lampetra fluviatilis L.*)," *Pubbl. Staz. Zool. Napoli*, **19:** 48–55.

MORGAN, T. H., 1923. "Removal of the block to self-fertilization in the Ascidian *Ciona*," *Proc. Natl. Acad. Sci.*, **9:** 170–171.

MOSER, F., 1939. "Studies on cortical layer response to stimulating agents in the *Arbacia* eggs. 1. Response to insemination," *J. Exp. Zool.*, **80:** 423–446.

MOTOMURA, I., 1941. "Materials of the fertilization membrane in the eggs of echinoderms," *Sci. Rep. Tôhoku Imp. Univ.*, **16:** 345–363.

———, 1954. "Parthenogenetic activation with potassium permanganate in the eggs of the bivalve and the sea urchin," *Sci. Rep. Tôhoku Univ.*, Ser. 4, **20:** 213–218.

MÜHLETHALER, K., and LINSKENS, H. F., 1956. "Elektronenmikroskopische Aufnahmen von Pollenschläuchen," *Experientia*, **12,** 253–254.

MULLINS, L. J., 1960. "An analysis of pore size in excitable membranes," *J. Gen. Physiol.*, Suppl. 1st, **43:** 105–117.

NAKANO, E., 1953. "Respiration during maturation and at fertilization of fish eggs," *Embryologia*, **2:** 21–31.

———, 1956. "Changes in the egg membrane of the fish egg during fertilization," *Embryologia*, **3:** 89–103.

———, GIUDICE, G., and MONROY, A., 1958. "On the incorporation of S^{35}-methionine in artificially activated sea urchin eggs," *Experientia*, **14:** 11–13.

———, and MONROY, A., 1958a. "Incorporation of S^{35}-methionine in the cell fractions of sea urchin eggs and embryos," *Exptl. Cell Res.*, **14:** 236–244.

———, ———, 1958b. "Some observations on the metabolism of S^{35}-methionine during development of the sea urchin egg," *Experientia*, **14:** 367–371.

———, and OHASHI, S., 1954. "On the carbohydrate component of the jelly coat and related substances of eggs from Japanese sea urchins," *Embryologia*, **2:** 81–86.

NEMER, M., 1962a. "Characteristics of the utilization of nucleosides by embryos of *Paracentrotus lividus*," *J. Biol. Chem.*, **237:** 143–149.

———, 1962b. "Interrelation of messenger polyribonucleotides and ribosomes in the sea urchin egg during embryonic development," *Biochem. Biophys. Res. Comm.*, **8:** 511–515.

———, 1963. "Old and new RNA in the embryogenesis of the purple sea urchin," *Proc. Natl. Acad. Sci.*, **50:** 230–235.

———, and BARD, S. G., 1963. "Polypeptide synthesis in sea urchin embryogenesis: an examination with synthetic polynucleotides," *Science*, **140:** 664–666.

NOLL, H., STAEHELIN, TH., and WETTSTEIN, F. O., 1963. "Ribosomal aggregates engaged in protein synthesis: ergosome breakdown and messenger ribonucleic acid transport," *Nature*, **198:** 632–638.

NOVIKOFF, A. B., 1939. "Surface changes in unfertilized and fertilized eggs of *Sabellaria vulgaris," J. Exp. Zool.*, **82**: 217–237.

NUMANOI, H., 1959a. "Studies on the fertilization substance. 8. Enzymic degradation of lecithin during development of sea urchin eggs," *Sci. Pap. Coll. Gen. Educ. Univ. Tokyo*, **9**: 285–296.

———, 1959b. "Studies on the fertilization substance. 9. Effect of intermediates split from the lecithin in sea urchin eggs during fertilization," *Sci. Pap. Coll. Gen. Educ. Univ. Tokyo*, **9**: 297–301.

ÖHMAN, L. O., 1944. "On the lipids of the sea urchin egg," *Ark. f. Zool.* **36 A**: No. 7.

OHNISHI, T., 1963. "Adenosinetriphosphatase activity relating to active transport in the cortex of sea urchin eggs," *J. Biochem.*, **53**: 238–241.

———, and SUGIYAMA, M., 1963. "Polarographic studies of oxygen uptake of sea urchin eggs," *Embryologia*, **8**: 79–88.

OKAZAKI, R., 1956. "On the possible role of high energy phosphate in the cortical change of sea urchin eggs. 1. Effect of dinitrophenol and sodium azide. 2. Effect of Uranly nitrate," *Exptl. Cell Res.*, **10**: 476–504.

ÖRSTRÖM, Å., 1941a. "Ueber die chemischen Vorgänge, insbesondere den Amoniakstoffwechsel bei der Entwicklungserregung des Seeigeleies," *Z. f. physiol. Chem.* **271**: 1–176.

———, 1941b. "Ueber die Stickstoff-fraktionen im Ei von *Paracentrotus lividus* vor und nach der Entwicklungserregung und ueber ihre Bedeutung für den osmotischen Druck und den Stoffwechsel," *Ark. Kemi, Mineral. o. Geol.*, **15 A**: No. 1.

———, and LINDBERG, O., 1940. "Ueber den Kohlenhydratstoffwechsel bei der Befruchtung des Seeigeleis," *Enzymologia*, **8**: 367–384.

———, and ÖRSTRÖM, M., 1942. "Ueber die Bindung von Kalzium in Ei und Larve von *Paracentrotus lividus," Protoplasma*, **36**: 475–490.

OSANAI, K., 1960a. "On the cortical granules of the toad egg," *Sci. Rep. Tôhoku Univ.*, Ser. IV, **26**: 69–75.

———, 1960b. "Development of the sea urchin egg with the inhibited breakdown of the cortical granules," *Sci. Rep. Tôhoku Univ.*, Ser. IV, **26**: 77–87.

PASTEELS, J. J., 1963. "Sur l'origine de la membrane nucléaire du pronucleus ♂ chez le Mollusque bivalve, *Barnea candida," Bull. Classe Sci. Acad. Royale Belgique*, **49**: 329–336.

———, CASTIAUX, P., and VANDERMEERSSCHE, G., 1959. "Ultrastructure du cytoplasme et distribution de l'acide ribonucléique dans l'oeuf fécondé, tant normal que centrifugé de *Paracentrotus lividus," Arch. Biol.* (Liège), **69**: 627–643.

———, and DE HARVEN, E., 1962. "Etude au microscope électronique du cortex de l'oeuf de *Barnea candida* (Mollusque bivalve) et son évolution au moment de la fécondation, de la maturation et de la segmentation," *Arch. de Biol. (Liège)*, **73**: 465–490.

140 · REFERENCES

PERLMANN, P., 1959. "Immunochemical analysis of the surface of the sea urchin egg: an approach to the study of fertilization," *Experientia*, 15: 41–52.

PFEFFER, W., 1884. "Locomotorische Richtungsbewegungen durch chemische Reize," *Unt. Bot. Inst. Tübingen*, 1: 363–481.

PHILIPS, F. S., 1940. "Oxygen consumption and its inhibition in the development of *Fundulus* and various pelagic eggs," *Biol. Bull.*, 78: 256–274.

PICKEN, E. L. R., and ROTHSCHILD, LORD, 1948. "Vapour pressure changes in the frog's egg at fertilization," *J. Exp. Biol.*, 25: 227–236.

PINCUS, G., and ENZMANN, E. V., 1932. "Fertilization in rabbit," *J. Exp. Biol.*, 9: 403–408.

POPA, G. T., 1927. "The distribution of substances in the spermatozoon (*Arbacia* and *Nereis*) ," *Biol. Bull.*, 52: 238–257.

POST, R. L., MERRITT, C. R., KINSOLVING, C. R., and ALBRIGHT, C. D., 1960. "Membrane adenosine triphosphatase as a participant in the active transport of sodium and potassium in the human erythrocyte," *J. Biol. Chem.*, 235: 1796–1802.

RAPKINE, L., 1931. "Sur les processus chimiques au cours de la division cellulaire," *Ann. physiol. physicochim. Biol.*, 7: 382–417.

REBHUN, L. I., 1962a. "Electron microscope studies on the vitelline membrane of the surf clam, *Spisula solidissima*," *J. Ultrastr. Res.*, 6: 107–122.

———, 1962b. "Dispersal of the vitelline membrane of the eggs of *Spisula solidissima* by alkaline, isotonic NaCl," *J. Ultrastr. Res.*, 6: 123–134.

REVERBERI, G., 1933. "Esperimenti di incrocio fra uova di *Ciona intestinalis* e spermi di *Phallusia mamillata*," *Rend. R. Accad. Naz. Lincei*, 17: 737–739.

———, 1936. "La segmentazione dei frammenti dell'uovo non fecondato di *Ascidia*," *Pubbl. Staz. Zool. Napoli*, 15: 198–216.

RICOTTA, C. M., 1956. "Increase of the non-protein amino-nitrogen in sea urchin eggs upon fertilization," *Naturwiss.*, 43: 258–259.

ROTHSCHILD, LORD, 1949. "The metabolism of fertilized and unfertilized sea urchin eggs. The action of light and carbon monoxide," *J. Exp. Biol.*, 26: 100–111.

———, 1952. "The behaviour of spermatozoa in the neighborhood of egg," *Internatl. Rev. Cytol.*, 1: 257–263.

———, 1956. "The physiology of sea urchin spermatozoa. Action of pH, dinitrophenol, dinitrophenol + versene, and usnic acid on O_2 uptake," *J. Exp. Biol.*, 33: 155–173.

———, and BARNES, H., 1953. "The inorganic constituents of the sea urchin egg," *J. Exp. Biol.*, 30: 534–544.

———, and SWANN, M. M., 1949. "The fertilization reaction in the sea urchin egg. A propagated response to sperm attachment," *J. Exp. Biol.*, 26: 164–176.

———, ———, 1950. "The fertilization reaction in the sea urchin egg. The effect of nicotine," *J. Exp. Biol.*, 27: 400–406.

———, ———, 1951a. "The conduction time of the block to polyspermy in the sea urchin egg," *Exptl. Cell Res.*, 2: 137.

———, ———, 1951b. "The fertilization reaction in the sea urchin. The probability of a successful sperm-egg collision," *J. Exp. Biol.*, 28: 403–416.

———, ———, 1952. "The fertilization reaction in the sea urchin. The block to polyspermy," *J. Exp. Biol.*, **29:** 469–483.

———, and TYLER, A., 1958. "The oxidation metabolism of eggs of *Urechis caupo*," *Biol. Bull.*, **115:** 136–146.

RUNNSTRÖM, J., 1928. "Ueber die Veränderung der Plasmakolloide bei der Entwicklungserregung des Seeigeleies. I," *Protoplasma*, **4:** 388–514.

———, 1930. "Atmungsmechanismus und Entwicklungserregung bei dem Seeigelei," *Protoplasma*, **10:** 106–173.

———, 1933. "Zur Kenntnis der Stoffwechselvorgänge bei der Entwicklungserregung des Seeigeleis," *Biochem. Ztsch.*, **258:** 257–279.

———, 1948. "On the action of trypsin and chymotrypsin on the unfertilized sea urchin eggs. A study concerning the mechanism of formation of the fertilization membrane," *Ark. f. Zool.*, **40 A:** Nr. 17.

———, 1956. "Some considerations on metabolic changes occurring at fertilization and during early development of the sea urchin egg," *Pubb. Staz. Zool. Napoli*, **28:** 315–340.

———, and KRISZAT, G., 1952. "The cortical propagation of the activation impulse in the sea urchin egg," *Exptl. Cell Res.*, **3:** 419–426.

———, MONNÉ, L., and BROMAN, L., 1943. "On some properties of the surface layers in the sea urchin egg and their changes upon activation," *Ark. f. Zool.*, **35 A:** Nr. 3.

———, ———, and WICKLUND, E., 1944. "Mechanism of formation of the fertilization membrane in the sea urchin egg," *Nature*, **153:** 313.

———, TISELIUS, A., and VASSEUR, E., 1942. "Zur Kenntnis der Gamonwirkungen bei *Psammechinus miliaris* und *Echinocardium chordatum*," *Ark. f. Kemi, Min. o. Geol.*, **15:** Nr. 16.

SAKAI, H., 1960. "Studies on sulphydryl groups during cell division of sea urchin egg. 3. -SH groups of KCl-soluble proteins and their change during cleavage," *J. Bioph. Bioch. Cytol.*, **8:** 609–615.

———, and DAN, K., 1959. "Studies on sulphydryl groups during cell division of sea urchin egg," *Exptl. Cell Res.*, **16:** 24–41.

SAKAI, Y. T., 1961. "Method for removal of chorion and fertilization of the naked egg in *Oryzias latipes*," *Embryologia*, **5:** 357–368.

SALZEN, E. A., 1957. "The density of sea urchin eggs, embryos and larvae," *Exptl. Cell Res.*, **12:** 615–625.

SCARANO, E., 1958. "5'-Deoxycytidylic acid deaminase enzymic production of 5'-deoxyuridylic acid," *Biochim. Biophys. Acta*, **29:** 459.

———, and MAGGIO, R., 1957. "An exchange between P^{32} labelled pyrophosphate and ATP catalyzed by amino acids in unfertilized sea urchin eggs," *Exptl. Cell Res.*, **12:** 403–405.

———, ———, 1959a. "Enzymatic deamination of 5-Methyldeoxy-cytidylic acid to thymidylic acid," *Arch. Bioch. Bioph.*, **79:** 392–393.

———, ———, 1959b. "The enzymatic deamination of 5'-deoxy-cytidylic acid and of 5'-methyl-deoxy-cytidylic acid in the developing sea urchin embryo," *Exptl. Cell Res.*, **18:** 333–346.

SCHARTAU, O., and MONTALENTI, G., 1941. "Le sostanze (gamoni) che intervengono nella fecondazione dell'uovo di Lampreda," *Boll. Soc. Ital. Biol. Sperim.*, **XVI:** 460.

SCHULZ, F. N., and BECKER, M., 1935. "Ueber die Kohlehydrate der Eiweissdrüse von *Rana esculenta,*" *Bioch. Ztsch.*, **280:** 217–226.

SELENKA, E., 1878. "Befruchtung des Eies von *Toxopneustes variegatus,*" Leipzig.

SESHACHAR, B. R., and BAGGA, S., 1963. "Cytochemistry of the oocyte of *Lovis tardigradus lydekkerianus* (Cebr.) and *Macaca mulatta mulatta* (Zimmerman) ," *J. Morphol.*, **113:** 119–137.

SHAVER, J. R., BARCH, S. H., and SHIVERS, C. A., 1962. "Tissue specificity of frog egg-jelly antigens," *J. Exp. Zool.*, **151:** 95–104.

SHIVERS, C. A. and METZ, CH. B., 1962. "Inhibition of fertilization in frog eggs by univalent fragments of rabbit antibody," *Proc. Soc. Exper. Biol. Med.* **110:** 385–387.

SKOU, J. C., 1957. "The influence of some cations on an adenosine triphosphatase from peripheral nerves," *Biochim. Biophys. Acta*, **23:** 394–401.

SLATER, E. C., and HÜLSMANN, W. C., 1959. "Control of rate of intracellular respiration," pp. 58–83 in G. E. W. Wolstenholme, and C. M. O'Connor, eds., *Ciba Foundation Symp. on Regulation of Cell Metabolism*, London: Churchill.

SOTELO, J. R., and PORTER, K. R., 1959. "An electron microscope study of the rat ovum," *J. Bioph. Bioch. Cytol.*, **5:** 327–341.

SPIKES, J. D., 1949. "Metabolism of sea urchin sperm," *The Amer. Nat.*, **83:** 285–301.

STAEHELIN, T., BRINTON, C. C., WETTSTEIN, F. O., and NOLL, H., 1963. "Structure and function of *E. coli* ergosomes," *Nature*, **199:** 865–870.

STEFANELLI, A., 1938. "Il metabolismo dell'uovo e dell'embrione studiato negli *Anfibi Anuri*. II. L'assunzione di ossigeno," *Arch. Sc. Biol.*, **24:** 411–441.

SUGIYAMA, M., 1951. "Re-fertilization of the fertilized eggs of the sea urchin," *Biol. Bull.*, **101:** 335–344.

———, 1953a. "Physiological analysis of the cortical response of the sea urchin egg to stimulating reagents. I. Response to sodium choleinate and wasp venom," *Biol. Bull.*, **104:** 210–215.

———, 1953b. "Physiological analysis of the cortical response of the sea urchin egg to stimulating reagents. II. The propagating or non-propagating nature of the cortical changes induced by various reagents," *Biol. Bull.*, **104:** 216–223.

———, 1956. "Physiological analysis of the cortical response of the sea urchin eggs," *Exptl. Cell Res.*, **10:** 364–376.

SUZUKI, R., 1958. "Sperm activation and aggregation during fertilization in some fishes. I. Behaviour of spermatozoa around the micropyle," *Embryologia*, **4:** 93–102.

———, 1959a. "Sperm activation and aggregation during fertilization in some fishes. II. Effect of distilled water on the sperm-stimulating capacity and fertilizability," *Embryologia*, **4:** 359–367.

———, 1959b. "Sperm activation and aggregation during fertilization in some fishes. III. Non species-specificity of stimulating factor," *Ann. Zool. Japon.*, **32:** 105–111.

———, 1960. "Sperm activation and aggregation during fertilization in some fishes. IV. Effects of pH, heat and other agents upon sperm-stimulating factor," *Jap. J. Zool.*, **12:** 465–476.

SZOLLOSI, D. G., and RIS, H., 1961. "Observation on sperm penetration in the rat," *J. Bioph. Bioch. Cytol.*, **10:** 275–283.

TYLER, A., 1939a. "Extraction of an egg membrane-lysin from sperm of the giant keyhole limpet *(Megathura crenulata),*" *Proc. Natl. Acad. Sci.*, **25:** 317–323.

———, 1939b. "Crystalline echinochrome and spinochrome: their failure to stimulate the respiration of eggs and sperm of *Strongylocentrotus,*" *Proc. Natl. Acad. Sci.*, **25:** 523–528.

———, 1940. "Sperm agglutination in the keyhole limpet, *Megathura crenulata,*" *Biol. Bull.*, **78:** 159–178.

———, 1941. "The role of fertilizin in the fertilization of eggs of the sea urchin and other animals," *Biol. Bull.*, **81:** 190–204.

———, 1946. "Loss of fertilizing power of sea urchin and *Urechis* sperm treated with "univalent" antibodies vs. antifertilizin," *Proc. Soc. Exp. Biol. Med.*, **62:** 197–199.

———, 1948. "On the chemistry of the fertilizin of the sea urchin *Strongylocentrotus purpuratus,*" *Anat. Rec.*, **101** (Suppl.) : 8–9.

———, 1949. "Properties of fertilizin and related substances of eggs and sperm of marine animals," *The Am. Nat.*, **83:** 195–219.

———, 1950. "Extension of the functional life span of spermatozoa by amino acids and peptides," *Biol. Bull.*, **99:** 324.

———, 1953. "Prolongation of life-span of sea urchin spermatozoa, and improvement of the fertilization-reaction, by treatment of spermatozoa and eggs with metal-chelating agents (amino acids, versene, dedtc, oxine, cupron) ," *Biol. Bull.*, **104:** 224–239.

———, 1956. "Physico-chemical properties of the fertilizins of the sea urchin *Arbacia punctulata* and the sand dollar *Echinarachnius parma,*" *Exptl. Cell Res.*, **10:** 377–386.

———, 1959. "Some immunological experiments of fertilization and early development in sea urchins," *Exptl. Cell. Res.*, Suppl. **7:** 183–199.

———, 1960. "Introductory remarks on theory of fertilization," pp. 155–174 in S. Ranzi, ed., *Symp. on Germ Cells and Dev.*, Pallanza.

———, 1962. "Introductory Remarks" in *Proc. Conference on Immuno Reproduction*, The Population Council, New York, pp. 13–15.

———, 1963. "The manipulations of macromolecular substances during fertilization and early development of animal eggs," *Amer. Zool.*, **3:** 109–126.

———, BURBANK, A., and TYLER, J. S., 1954. "The electrophoretic mobilities of the fertilizin of *Arbacia* and *Echinarachnius,*" *Biol. Bull.*, **107:** 304.

———, and FOX, S. W., 1940. "Evidence for the protein nature of the sperm agglutinins of the keyhole limpet and sea urchin," *Biol. Bull.*, **79:** 153–165.

———, and HATHAWAY, R. R., 1958. "Production of ^{35}S-labelled fertilizin in eggs of *Arbacia punctulata*," *Biol. Bull.*, 115: 369.

———, and HUMASON, W. D., 1937. "On the energetics of differentiation. 6. Comparison of the temperature coefficients of the respiratory rates of unfertilized and fertilized eggs," *Biol. Bull.*, 73: 261–279.

———, and METZ, CH. B., 1955. "Effects of fertilizin treatment of sperm and trypsin-treatment of eggs on homologous and cross-fertilization in sea urchin," *Pubbl. Staz. Zool. Napoli*, 27: 128–145.

———, and MONROY, A., 1955. "Apparent and real microinjection of echinoderm eggs," *Biol. Bull.*, 109: 370.

———, ———, 1959. "Changes in rate of transfer of potassium across the membrane upon fertilization of eggs of *Arbacia punctulata*," *J. Exper. Zool.*, 142: 675–690.

———, ———, KAO, C. Y., and GRUNDFEST, H., 1956. "Membrane potential and resistance of the starfish egg before and after fertilization," *Biol. Bull.*, 111: 153–177.

———, ———, and METZ, CH. B., 1956. "Fertilization of fertilized sea urchin eggs," *Biol. Bull.*, 110: 184–195.

———, SEATON, A., and SIGNORET, J., 1961. "Further analysis of antidevelopmental action of antisera against fertilizins and against other egg extracts of sea urchins," *Amer. Zool.*, 1: 394.

UNGAR, G., ASCHHEIM, E., PSYCHOYOS, S., and ROMANO, D. V., 1957. "Reversible changes of protein configuration in stimulated nerve structures," *J. Gen. Physiol.*, 40: 635–652.

VASSEUR, E., 1947. "The sulphuric acid content of the egg coat of the sea urchin *Strongylocentrotus droebachiensis* Müll.," *Ark. Kemi, Min. o. Geol.*, 25B: Nr. 6.

———, 1949a. "The effect of sea urchin jelly coat solution and calcium ions on the oxygen uptake of sea urchin sperm," *Ark. Kemi*, 1: 393–399.

———, 1949b. "Chemical studies on the jelly coat of the sea urchin egg," *Acta Chem. Scand.*, 2: 900–913.

———, 1950. "L-Galactose in the jelly coat of *Echinus esculentus*," *Acta Chem. Scand.*, 4: 1144–1145.

———, 1951. "Demonstration of a jelly-splitting enzyme at the surface of the sea urchin spermatozoon," *Exptl. Cell Res.*, 2: 144–146.

———, 1952. "Periodate oxidation of the jelly coat substance of *Echinocardium cordatum*," *Acta Chem. Scand.*, 6: 376.

———, 1954. "The chemistry and physiology of the jelly coat of the sea urchin egg," 32 pp. *Kihlströmstryck.* A. B. Stockholm.

———, and HAGSTRÖM, B., 1946. "On the gamones of some sea urchins from the Swedish West coast," *Ark. f. Zool.*, 37 A: Nr. 17.

———, and IMMERS, J., 1949. "Hexosamine in the sea urchin egg jelly coat: a misinterpretation of the method of Elson and Morgan," *Ark. f. Kemi*, 1: 253.

VELDHUISEN, G., JANSZ, H. S., ATEN, J. B. T., POUWELS, P. M., OOSTERBAN, R. A., and COHEN, J. A., 1962. "Bacteriophage transformation: biological activity of fragments of DNA of bacteriophage T 4," *Biochim. Biophys. Acta,* **61:** 630–632.

VINCENT, W. S., 1963. "Functions of the nucleolus," *Proceedings 11th Internatl. Congress Genetics.*

WADA, S. K., COLLIER, J. R., and DAN, J. C., 1956. "Studies on the acrosome. V. An egg-membrane lysin from the acrosomes of *Mytilus edulis* spermatozoa," *Exptl. Cell Res.,* **10:** 168–180.

WARBURG, O., 1910. "Ueber die Oxydationen in lebenden Zellen nach Versuchen am Seeigelei," *Ztsch. f. physiol. Chemie,* **66:** 305–340.

WARNER, J. R., KNOPF, P. M., and RICH, A., 1963. "A multiple ribosomal structure in protein synthesis," *Proc. Natl. Acad. Sci.,* **49:** 122–129.

———, RICH, A., and HALL, C. E., 1962. "Electron microscope studies of ribosomal clusters synthesizing hemoglobin," *Science,* **138:** 1399–1403.

WEINSTEIN, I. B., SCHECHTER, A. N., BURKA, E. R., and MARKS, P. A., 1963. "Reticulocytes protein synthesis: response of ribosome fractions to polyuridylic acid," *Science,* **140:** 314–316.

WETTSTEIN, F. O., STAEHELIN, TH., and NOLL, H., 1963. "Ribosomal aggregates engaged in protein synthesis: characterization of the ergosome," *Nature,* **197:** 430–435.

WHITAKER, D. M., 1931a. "On the rate of oxygen consumption by fertilized and unfertilized eggs. 1. *Fucus vesciculosus,*" *J. Gen. Physiol.,* **15:** 167–182.

———, 1931b. "On the rate of oxygen consumption by fertilized and unfertilized eggs. 2. *Cumingia tellinoides,*" *J. Gen. Physiol.,* **15:** 183–190.

———, 1931c. "On the rate of oxygen consumption by fertilized and unfertilized eggs. 3. *Nereis limbata,*" *J. Gen. Physiol.,* **15:** 191–200.

———, 1933a. "On the rate of oxygen consumption by fertilized and unfertilized eggs. 4. *Chaetopterus* and *Arbacia punctalata,*" *J. Gen. Physiol.,* **16:** 475–495.

———, 1933b. "On the rate of oxygen consumption by fertilized and unfertilized eggs. 5. Comparison and interpretation," *J. Gen. Physiol.,* **16:** 497–528.

WHITELEY, A. H., and CHAMBERS, E. L., 1960. "The differentiation of a phosphate transport mechanism in the fertilized egg of the sea urchin," pp. 387–401 in S. Ranzi, ed., *Symp. on Germ Cells and Development,* Pallanza.

WIESE, L., and JONES, R. F., 1963. "Studies on gamete copulation in heterothallic Chlamidomonads," *J. Cell Comp. Physiol.,* **61:** 265–274.

WILSON, E. B., 1901. "Experimental studies in cytology. 1. A cytological study of artificial parthenogenesis in sea urchin eggs," *Arch. f. Entw. mech.,* **12:** 559–596.

———, 1903. "Experiments on cleavage and localization in the nemertine egg," *Arch. f. Entw. mech.,* **16:** 411–460.

———, and MATHEWS, A. P., 1895. "Maturation, fertilization and polarity in the echinoderm egg. New light on the 'quadrille of the centers'," *J. Morphol.,* **10:** 319–342.

WILT, F. H., 1963. "The synthesis of ribonucleic acid in sea urchin embryos," *Bioch. Bioph. Res. Comm.,* **11:** 447–451.

———, 1964. "Ribonucleic acid synthesis during sea urchin embryogenesis," *Dev. Biology*, 9: 299–313.

———, and HULTIN, T., 1962. "Stimulation of phenylalanine incorporation by polyuridylic acid in homogenates of sea urchin eggs," *Bioch. Bioph. Res. Comm.*, 9: 313–317.

WOLPERT, L., and MERCER, E. H., 1961. "An electron microscope study of fertilization of the sea urchin egg *Psammechinus miliaris*," *Exptl. Cell Res.*, 22: 45–55.

YAMAMOTO, T., 1944. "Physiological studies on fertilization and activation of fish eggs. 1. Response of the cortical layer of the egg of *Oryzias latipes* to insemination and to artificial stimulation. 2. The conduction of the "fertilization-wave" in the egg of *Oryzias latipes*," *Ann. Zool. Jap.*, 22: 109–136.

YAMANE, I., 1930. "The proteolytic action of mammalian spermatozoa and its bearing upon the second maturation division of ova," *Cytologia*, 1: 394–403.

———, 1935. "Kausal analytische Studien über die Befruchtung des Kanincheneies. I. Die Dispersion der Follikelzellen und die Ablösung der Zellen der Corona radiata des Eies durch Spermatozoen," *Cytologia*, 6: 233–255.

YANAGIMACHI, R., 1957a. "Studies of fertilization in *Clupea pollasii*. 1. Extension of fertilizable life of the unfertilized eggs by means of isotonic Ringer's solution," *Zool. Mag.*, 66: 218–221. (in Japanese).

———, 1957b. "Studies of fertilization in *Clupea pollasii*. 2. Structure and activity of spermatozoa," *Zool. Mag.*, 66: 222–225. (in Japanese).

———, 1957c. "Studies of fertilization in *Clupea pollasii*. 3. Manner of sperm entrance into the egg," *Zool. Mag.*, 66: 226–233. (in Japanese).

———, and KANOH, Y., 1953. "Manner of sperm entry in herring egg with special reference to the role of calcium ions in fertilization," *J. Fac. Sci. Hokkaido Univ.*, Ser. VI, Zool., 11: 487.

YASUMASU, I., and KOSHIHARA, H., 1963. "Amino acyl RNA and transfer enzyme in sea urchin eggs," *Zool. Mag.*, 72: 259–262. (in Japanese).

———, and NAKANO, E., 1963. "Respiratory level of sea urchin eggs before and after fertilization," *Biol. Bull.*, 125: 182–187.

YATZU, N., 1905. "The formation of centrosomes in enucleated egg fragments," *J. Exp. Zool.*, 2: 287–312.

YCAS, M., 1954. "The respiratory and glycolytic enzymes of sea urchin eggs," *J. Exp. Biol.*, 31: 208–217.

ZEUTHEN, E., 1944. "Oxygen uptake during mitosis. Experiments on the eggs of the frog *(Rana platyrrhina),*" *C. R. Trav. Lab. Carlsberg*, Sér. Chim., 25: 191–228.

ZOTIN, A. I., 1958. "The mechanism of hardening of the salmonid egg membrane after fertilization or spontaneous activation," *J. Embryol. exp. Morphol.*, 6: 546–568.

index